NEW YORK GRAPHIC SOCIETY

FINE ART COLLECTIONS

GREENWICH, CONNECTICUT, U.S.A.
NEW YORK, CHICAGO, DALLAS
HIGH POINT

A CHARTWELL COMPANY

NEW YORK GRAPHIC SOCIETY LTD.

Main Office:

For Mail:

P.O. Box 1469
Greenwich, CT 06836
(203) 661-2400
(212) 933-1134

For Deliveries:

35 River Road
Cos Cob, CT 06807

Showrooms:

200 Lexington Avenue
Room 809
New York, New York 10016
(212) 696-4350

1256 Merchandise Mart
Chicago, Illinois 60654
(312) 644-3170

World Trade Center
Space 9004
Dallas, Texas 75258
(214) 742-7126

Southern Furniture Market Center
210 East Commerce — G 261
Highpoint, North Carolina 27260
(919) 889-9084

International Standard Book Number 0-8212-1644-9
Library of Congress Catalog Card Number 86-61502
Copyright © 1986 New York Graphic Society Ltd.
Printed in the United States, 1986

Note from the Publisher

New York Graphic Society, for over sixty years the world's leading publisher of fine art, continues the tradition with this new *Fine Art Collections* catalogue. It is our hope that these more than 2,000 images, including our best-known reproductions and posters and a superb new offering of hand-colored etchings and engravings, will significantly enhance the beauty of any environment.

INTRODUCTION

This introduces the first edition of *Fine Art Collections,* the most comprehensive catalogue of fine art images ever published in a single book. With its expanded format of more than 2,000 images, hundreds added since our last catalogue, *Fine Art Collections* becomes the ultimate source for anyone seeking beautiful and decorative wall art.

New York Graphic Society has been the prominent name in art publishing for over sixty years. Our quality reproductions, long the mainstay of our company, have provided a complete reference of art history from old to modern masters. This tradition will, of course, continue.

Yet, with the advent of this new catalogue, we have achieved a greatly expanded scope of offerings. The name alone, *Fine Art Collections,* provides the first indication that this catalogue is composed of more than just reproductions. Indeed, the collection has grown with the times and now includes a new and diverse selection of posters. Among these are many traditional museum masterworks, colorful contemporary images, and the great photographic works of Ansel Adams. All offering the same high quality you have come to expect from us throughout the years.

Another first is a separate section of hand-colored etchings and engravings, the majority of which have been imported from fine European printing houses and produced from 17th, 18th, and 19th century antique plates. Each image is printed in black and white, then carefully colored by hand to maintain fidelity to the original work of art. Here you will find a wide variety of charming florals and botanicals, great English and French hunt scenes, unique 17th-century astronomy and zodiac maps, ancient sailing vessels and much more. This outstanding collection adds a new dimension to New York Graphic Society by offering a most desirable but often difficult to find fine art medium.

In reorganizing and editing *Fine Art Collections,* it was our goal to make this a more encompassing reference to better serve the needs of its varied users. For schools, libraries and museums we have provided a chronology of art from its pre-Christian beginnings through contemporary masterworks.

For the most part, however, *Fine Art Collections* will be used to select images for residential and commercial wall decor. With this in mind, we have added numerous artworks whose style and subject matter perfectly complement interior design creativity. They feature the colors and artistic trends that reflect today's many diverse tastes.

The *Fine Art Collections* catalogue will be available through thousands of fine art galleries and frame shops and to art consultants, interior designers, architects and contract specifiers.

To better serve the user and to make it easier to locate images, we have organized this new catalogue into sixteen clearly defined subject classifications. No longer, for example, will landscapes be found in various places throughout the volume. Instead, all landscapes, from traditional to abstract, will be grouped together in one easy-to-locate section. Other subject headings are: Portraits, Impressionism, Americana, Groups and Figures, Religious, Seascapes, American Folk and Primitive Art, Flowers and Fruit, Still Lifes, Abstract, Western, Animals, Orientals, and Hunting, Sports, and Games.

While *Fine Art Collections* is a catalogue that has responded to changing tastes and demographics, what has not changed is New York Graphic Society's commitment to quality. Whether it be the calibre of our artists, the printing standards we demand or the quality of paper we print on, the requirements have always been the highest. We publish art that passes the test of longevity and our images will be as desirable in future years as they are today. Many, in fact, have been in our catalogues more than thirty years.

New York Graphic Society has a heritage of publishing fine art with great fidelity to the original. With current advances in printing technology, our quality reproductions and posters remain unparalleled in the marketplace. It is our goal to continue this long tradition.

TABLE OF CONTENTS

POLICY and ORDER INFORMATION

Our telephone number is (203) 661-2400, in New York City (212) 933-1134. Orders may be placed with our sales representatives, by mail or directly by phone. Our Customer Service Department and order lines are open from 8:30 a.m. to 6:00 p.m. EST., Monday through Friday. Calls made after 6:00 P.M. will be recorded by our answering service and your call will be returned the following business day. Please refer to your customer number when placing orders.

Our minimum is $75.00 retail for opening orders and re-orders. If the minimum is not met, a $5.00 service charge will be applied to the order. There are no exceptions. The standard 50% discount applies to the retail trade. For quantity discounts, please consult your local New York Graphic Society sales representative or call us directly.

Please note, it is not our policy to offer items on consignment.

CREDIT

A credit application accompanies all opening orders. New accounts will be shipped on a prepaid or C.O.D. basis until a credit application is completed, returned and credit has been established. Net 30-day terms on all New York Graphic Society open accounts.

RETURNS

Please check shipments carefully upon receipt. If you receive a flawed image, we will exchange it for the same image in perfect condition. We must be notified within 5 days of receipt of invoice of any damages, flaws or incorrect images that are received. No credit will be issued if items are returned to us without authorization. No exchanges will be issued if items returned to us for any reason are not in resaleable condition.

If you receive a package that has been damaged in transit, do not accept this shipment and call us immediately.

Due to various printing methods employed, there may be instances where the color represented in the catalog does not match the actual reproduction. We cannot accept returns or exchanges based on these variations.

BACKORDERS

We do not backorder items that are out of stock at the time of the order unless specifically requested. When items must be backordered, they will appear on the original invoice as such, but are not billed until the backorder ships. The normal freight and handling charges apply to backorders.

SHIPPING

Orders are generally shipped within 24 hours of receipt. Standard method of shipping is UPS ground in the continental U.S.A. Shipments to California, Oregon and Washington ship UPS Blue Label unless otherwise requested. Packing lists are enclosed with orders shipping UPS ground. UPS services include Overnight and Second Day Air which must be requested when the order is placed. There is a $1.00 tube charge on all orders. Packaging charges are $2.00 for orders under $400.00 retail. Applicable C.O.D. charges are additional. All shipping charges will be posted to your invoice.

FOREIGN SHIPMENTS

Minimum opening order is $200.00 retail. All orders are payable in U.S. funds. All export orders must be prepaid before shipment. Orders shipped Air Parcel Post or seamail require prepayment of both order and shipping costs. If you prefer, shipments can be sent air freight collect by the freight forwarder of your choice. Please specify the method of shipping at the time the order is placed. Pro-forma invoices are available upon request. We ask that all correspondence be in English in order to avoid translation problems.

MEASUREMENTS

Although all images have been carefully measured minor variations may occur from the printed dimensions. We recommend that frames and mats not be cut until you have received your purchase.

CLASSIFIED SUBJECT MATTER INDEX

A Select Group of
OLD and MODERN MASTERS

Additional Masterworks are to be found throughout the Catalogue
listed by appropriate subject matter.

Marc Chagall, page 31

Leonardo da Vinci
MONA LISA, *1503*
Louvre Museum, Paris
3275 - 10″x6½″ (25x16 cm)
5217 - 18½″x12¾″ (47x32 cm)

Leonardo da Vinci *(Italian, 1452-1519)*
GINEVRA DE'BENCI, *c. 1480*
National Gallery of Art, Washington, D.C.
4506 - 15″x14¼″ (38x35 cm)

Pieter Brueghel, the Elder
THE WEDDING DANCE, *1566*
Detroit Institute of the Arts
4312 - 10½″x14″ (26x35 cm)

Pieter Brueghel, the Elder
VILLAGE WEDDING, *c. 1560*
Kunsthistorisches Museum, Vienna
4752 - 11″x14″ (28x35 cm)
5277 - 15″x21½″ (38x54 cm)

Pieter Brueghel, the Elder
PEASANTS' DANCE, *c. 1560*
Kunsthistorisches Museum, Vienna
4753 - 11″x14″ (28x35 cm)

Pieter Brueghel, the Elder
WINTER—HUNTERS IN THE SNOW, *1565*
Kunsthistorisches Museum, Vienna
4756 - 11″x14″ (28x35 cm)
9999 - 31¼″x43¾″ (79x111 cm)

Pieter Brueghel, the Elder *(Flemish, 1525-1569)*
THE FALL OF ICARUS, *c. 1555*
Royal Museum, Brussels
4754 - 11″x14″ (28x35 cm)

Pieter Brueghel, the Elder
THE HARVESTERS, *1565*
The Metropolitan Museum of Art, New York
4755 - 11″x14″ (28x35 cm)
(For sale in U.S.A. only)

Jan Vermeer
THE LACEMAKER, *c. 1660*
National Gallery of Art, Washington, D.C.
Mellon Collection
5641 - 17½"x15½" (44x39 cm)

Jan Vermeer
THE ARTIST'S STUDIO, *1665*
Kunsthistorisches Museum, Vienna
8749 - 31¼"x25¾" (79x65 cm)

Jan Vermeer
A WOMAN WEIGHING GOLD, *c. 1657*
National Gallery of Art, Washington, D.C.
Widener Collection
5254 - 16¼"x14½" (41x37 cm)

Jan Vermeer
GIRL WITH TURBAN, *1660*
Mauritshuis, The Hague, Holland
5785 - 19"x15½" (48x39 cm)

Jan Vermeer
THE MILKMAID, *c. 1656*
Rijksmuseum, Amsterdam
565 - 18"x16" (46x41 cm)

Rembrandt
YOUNG GIRL AT A WINDOW, *1645*
College Gallery, Dulwich, London
5230 - 18½″x16″ (47x40 cm)

Rembrandt
A GIRL WITH A BROOM, *1651*
National Gallery of Art, Washington, D.C.
Mellon Collection
7662 - 26″x22″ (66x56 cm)

Rembrandt
YOUNG GIRL AT AN OPEN HALF DOOR, *1645*
The Art Institute of Chicago
3525 - 9½″x8″ (24x20 cm)
4651 - 14″x11¾″ (35x30 cm)
7651 - 26″x22″ (66x56 cm)

Rembrandt Harmensz van Rijn *(Dutch, 1606-1669)*
THE MILL, *c. 1650*
National Gallery of Art, Washington, D.C.
Widener Collection
792 - 24¾″x30″ (63x76 cm)

Rembrandt
THE ARTIST'S SON, TITUS, *1655*
The Metropolitan Museum of Art, New York
4297 - 14″x10¼″ (35x26 cm)
7296 - 30½″x22¾″ (77x58 cm)

Rembrandt
THE POLISH RIDER, *c. 1655*
The Frick Collection, New York
403 - 11¾″x14″ (30x35 cm)
703 - 25″x29¼″ (63x74 cm)

Rembrandt
THE NIGHT WATCH, 1642
Rijksmuseum, Amsterdam
7660 - 23"x27¾" (58x70 cm)

Rembrandt
HENDRIKJE STOFFELS, *c. 1652-54*
Mrs. Norton Simon, Los Angeles
6863 - 26"x21½" (66x54 cm)

Rembrandt
PORTRAIT OF THE ARTIST'S SON TITUS, *undated*
The Norton Simon Collection
4220 - 14"x11¾" (35x30 cm)
7664 - 25¼"x21¼" (64x54 cm)

Rembrandt
MASTERS OF THE CLOTH GUILD, *1661-62*
Rijksmuseum, Amsterdam
7483 - 20¼"x29¾" (51x75 cm)

Rembrandt
PORTRAIT OF A RABBI, *1657*
California Palace of Legion of Honor, San Francisco
Mildred Anna Williams Fund, 1948
*809 - 28"x23" (71x58 cm)

Rembrandt
THE PHILOSOPHER, *c. 1650*
National Gallery of Art, Washington, D.C.
Widener Collection
6621 - 24"x18¾" (61x47 cm)

Francisco de Goya
THE BULLFIGHT, *1810-15*
The Metropolitan Museum of Art, New York
6294 - 18¾"x24¼" (47x61 cm)

Francisco de Goya
GOSSIPING WOMEN, *1787-91*
Wadsworth Atheneum, Hartford, Connecticut
9833 - 16"x40" (41x101 cm)

Pablo Picasso
THE GOURMET, *1901*
National Gallery of Art, Washington, D.C.
Chester Dale Collection
7685 - 28″x20½″ (71x52 cm)

Pablo Picasso *(Spanish, 1881-1973)*
BLUE BOY, *1905*
Collection Mr. and Mrs. M.M. Warburg, New York
4807 - *(bust detail)* 14″x11″ (35x28 cm)
6807 - 24″x13¼″ (61x33 cm)

Pablo Picasso
STILL LIFE WITH MANDOLIN, *1923*
Private Collection
7075 - 20½″x28″ (52x71 cm)

Pablo Picasso
HARLEQUIN AND BOY, 1905
(Study for "Family of Saltimbanques")
The Baltimore Museum of Art
Cone Collection
682 - 23¼"x18½" (59x47 cm)

Pablo Picasso
HARLEQUIN ON HORSEBACK, 1905
Collection Mr. and Mrs. Paul Mellon
6854 - 24"x16½" (61x42 cm)

Pablo Picasso
HARLEQUIN, *1917*
Picasso Museum, Barcelona
728 - 28½"x22" (73x55 cm)

Pablo Picasso
TWO HARLEQUINS, *1905*
The Stephen C. Clark Collection, New York
4006 - 14"x9¾" (35x25 cm)

Pablo Picasso
BOY WITH CATTLE, *1906*
The Columbus Gallery of Fine Arts
Howald Collection
6358 - 23½"x18½" (59x47 cm)

Pablo Picasso
PIERROT WITH FLOWERS, *1929*
Estate of the Artist
4326 - 15½"x11½" (39x29 cm)
7326 - 21"x15½" (53x39 cm)

Pablo Picasso
PIERROT WITH MASK, *1925*
Estate of the Artist
4325 - 15½"x11½" (39x29 cm)
7325 - 21"x15½" (53x39 cm)

Pablo Picasso
THE LITTLE SHEPHERD, *1923*
Estate of the Artist
4323 - 15½"x11½" (39x29 cm)
6323 - 21"x15½" (53x39 cm)

Pablo Picasso
THE ARTIST'S SON, *1924*
Estate of the Artist.
4324 - 15½"x11½" (39x29 cm)
7324 - 21"x15½" (53x39 cm)

Pablo Picasso
THE OLD GUITARIST, *1903*
The Art Institute of Chicago
4601 - 16¾"x11¼" (42x28 cm)
7341 - 30"x20" (76x51 cm)

Pablo Picasso
THE TRAGEDY, *1903*
National Gallery of Art, Washington, D.C.
Chester Dale Collection
6851 - 24"x15½" (61x39 cm)

Pablo Picasso
CORRIDA, *1960*
Galerie Louise Leiris
9089 - 12¼"x32" (31x81 cm)

Pablo Picasso
GUERNICA, *1937*
Museo del Prado, Cason del Buen Retiro, Madrid
5728 - 8½"x19" (22x49 cm)
9728 - 16"x35½" (40x90 cm)

Pablo Picasso
WAR, *1952*
Temple of Peace, Vallauris
9576 - 16¼"x35¾" (41x90 cm)

Amedeo Modigliani *(Italian, 1884-1920)*
PORTRAIT OF MADAME ZBOROWSKA, *1917-18*
Rhode Island School of Design
Museum of Art, Providence
5344 - 21"x16" (53x40 cm)

Amedeo Modigliani
GYPSY WOMAN WITH BABY, *1919*
National Gallery of Art, Washington, D.C.
Chester Dale Collection
6256 - 24"x15" (60x38 cm)

Marc Chagall
THE OPEN WINDOW
(Finestra Aperta)
Private Collection
6521 - 17¾"x22" (45x52 cm)

Marc Chagall
I AND THE VILLAGE, *1911*
The Museum of Modern Art, New York
3512 - 7½"x6" (19x15 cm)
7037 - 28"x22" (71x55 cm)

Marc Chagall
THE VIOLINIST, *1912-13*
Stedelijk Museum, Amsterdam
6238 - 23½"x20" (60x50 cm)

Marc Chagall
STILL LIFE WITH FLOWERS
Private Collection
6461 - 22¼"x17¾" (56x45 cm)

Marc Chagall
EVENING ENCHANTMENT, *1948*
Private Collection
6269 - 24"x20" (61x50 cm)

Marc Chagall
MORNING MYSTERY, *1948*
Private Collection
6270 - 23½"x19½" (60x50 cm)

Henri Matisse
STILL LIFE: APPLES ON PINK TABLECLOTH, *c. 1922*
National Gallery of Art, Washington, D.C.
Chester Dale Collection
7828 - 23"x28" (58x71 cm)

Henri Matisse
STILL LIFE WITH LEMONS, *1927*
Collection of Mr. and Mrs. Nathan Cummings
518 - 16"x19" (40x48 cm)

Henri Matisse *(French, 1869-1954)*
L'ESCARGOT, *1952*
The Tate Gallery, London
6523 - 21¼"x21½" (54x54½ cm)

Henri Matisse
LA DANSE
Grenoble Museum
7337 - 18″x23¾″ (45x60 cm)

Henri Matisse
FLOWER PETALS
5545 - 10½″x18″ (27x46 cm)
9085 - 11″x47″ (28x120 cm)

Charles Demuth
PAQUEBOT PARIS, *1921-22*
Columbus Gallery of Fine Arts
6389 - 25¼″x20¼″ (64x51 cm)

Fernand Léger *(French, 1881-1955)*
THE BLUE BASKET, *1949*
Private Collection
7289 - 24½″x19″ (63x48 cm)

Marcel Duchamp
CHOCOLATE GRINDER NO. 2, *1914*
Philadelphia Museum of Art
7523 - 24″x20″ (60x50 cm)

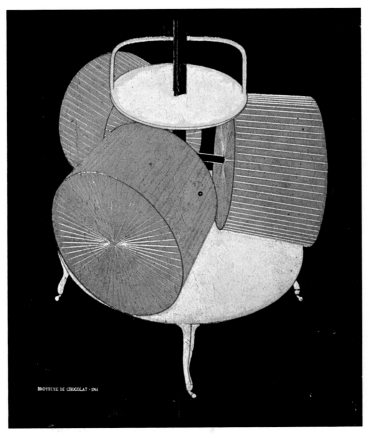

Edward Hopper
ROOMS BY THE SEA, *1951*
Yale University Art Gallery
Bequest of Stephen Carleton Clark
7670 - 21¾″x30″ (55x76 cm)

Will Barnet *(American, 1911-)*
STAIRWAY, *1970*
Private Collection
8517 - 24″x33″ (60x83 cm)

Maxfield Parrish
TRANQUILITY
Maxfield Parrish Estate Collection
7946 - 29½″x24″ (75x61 cm)

Maxfield Parrish *(American, 1870-1966)*
TWILIGHT
Private Collection
5535 - 14¾″x11¾″ (37x30 cm)
7945 - 22½″x18″ (57x46 cm)

Maxfield Parrish
DAYBREAK
5534 - 10½″x18″ (27x46 cm)
7977 - 17¾″x29¾″ (45x75 cm)

Maxfield Parrish (*American, 1870-1966*)
THE PRINCE
3975 - 12"x10" (30½x25½ cm)

Maxfield Parrish
GARDEN OF ALLAH
5943 - 9"x18" (23x45 cm)

Maxfield Parrish (*American, 1870-1966*)
THE LUTE PLAYERS
5930 - 10½"x18" (27x46 cm)

Wayne Thiebaud *(Contemporary American)*
YO-YOS, *1963*
Albright—Knox Gallery, Buffalo, N.Y.
Gift of Seymour H. Knox, 1953
6026 - 24″x24″ (61x61 cm)

Roy Lichtenstein *(American, 1923-   )*
MODERN PAINTING OF SUN RAYS, *1967*
The Joseph H. Hirshhorn Collection
9671 - 25½″x36″ (64x91 cm)

PORTRAITS

Sir Henry Raeburn,   page 44

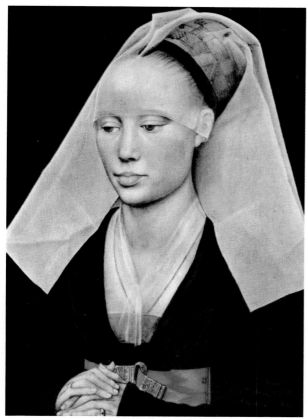

Rogier van der Weyden (Flemish 1399/1400-1464)
PORTRAIT OF A LADY, c. 1455
National Gallery of Art, Washington, D.C.
Mellon Collection
445 - 13¾"x9¾" (35x24 cm)

Hans Memling (Flemish, 1432-1494)
PORTRAIT OF A YOUNG MAN
Lehman Collection, New York
479 - 15"x10¾" (38x27 cm)

Joos van Cleve (Flemish, active 1511-1540/1)
JORIS W. VEZELER, c. 1520
National Gallery of Art, Washington, D.C.
Andrew W. Mellon Gift
6658 - 23¾"x16¾" (60x42 cm)

Joos van Cleve
MARGARETHA BOGHE,
WIFE OF JORIS W. VEZELER, c. 1520
National Gallery of Art, Washington, D.C.
Andrew W. Mellon Gift
6657 - 23½"x17" (59x43 cm)

Sir Henry Raeburn *(British, 1756-1823)*
THE REVEREND ROBERT WALKER
SKATING ON DUDDINGSTON LOCH
National Gallery of Scotland
6933 - 24¼″x20¼″ (62x52 cm)

Johannes Verspronk *(Dutch, 1597-1662)*
PORTRAIT OF A YOUNG GIRL, *1641*
Rijksmuseum, Amsterdam
5362 - 20″x15¾″ (51x40 cm)

Hans Holbein *(German, 1497-1543)*
SIR THOMAS MORE, *1527*
The Frick Collection, New York
708 - 29″x23″ (73x58 cm)

After: John Singleton Copley
ELIZABETH, THE ARTIST'S DAUGHTER, *1776-77*
National Gallery of Art, Washington, D.C.
Andrew Mellon Fund
6312 - 24"x13" (61x33 cm)

Unknown Colonial Artist
MRS. FREAKE AND BABY MARY, c. *1674*
Worcester Art Museum
6674 - 21"x18" (53x46 cm)

Velázquez
INFANTA MARGARITA THERESA, *1653*
Louvre Museum, Paris
5224 - 15¾"x13" (40x33 cm)

Théodore Géricault (French, *1791-1824*)
ENGLISH BOY, *1821*
The Norton Simon Collection
5685 - 18"x14" (46x35 cm)

Jean François Millet
YOUNG SHEPHERDESS
Museum of Fine Arts, Boston
6932 - 24″x16½″ (61x42 cm)

Sir Anthony van Dyck *(Flemish, 1599-1641)*
FILIPPO CATTANEO, SON OF MARCHESA
ELENA GRIMALDI, *1623*
National Gallery of Art, Washington, D.C.
Widener Collection
6494 - 24″x16½″ (61x42 cm)

John Hesselius *(American, 1728-1778)*
CHARLES CALVERT, *1761*
The Baltimore Museum of Art
6291 - 24″x19″ (61x48 cm)

Gustav C.L. Richter *(German, 1823-1884)*
THE ARTIST'S SISTER
National Gallery, Berlin
3137 - 11″x9″ (28x23 cm)
7507 - 27½″x22″ (70x56 cm)

Jean Etienne Liotard *(Swiss, 1702-1789)*
THE PAINTER'S NIECE, MLLE. LAVERGNE, *1746*
Staatliche Gemäldesammlungen, Dresden
5000 - 20″x15¾″ (51x40 cm)

Jean-Honoré Fragonard
A YOUNG GIRL READING, *1776*
National Gallery of Art, Washington, D.C.
4725 - 14″x11″ (35x28 cm)
6725 - 25¾″x20¼″ (65x51 cm)

Jean-Baptiste Siméon Chardin
THE KITCHEN MAID, *c. 1738*
National Gallery of Art, Washington, D.C.
Samuel H. Kress Collection
5100 - 17¾″x14¼″ (45x36 cm)

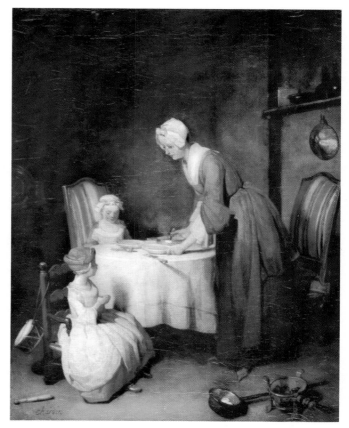

Jean-Baptiste Siméon Chardin
THE BLESSING, *1744*
Hermitage State Museum, Leningrad
5099 - 20″x15½″ (51x39 cm)

Peter Paul Rubens
LE CHAPEAU DE PAILLE, *c. 1620*
National Gallery, London
5219 - 18″x12½″ (46x32 cm)

Jacques Louis David *(French, 1748-1825)*
NAPOLEON IN HIS STUDY, *1812*
National Gallery of Art, Washington, D.C.
Samuel H. Kress Collection
4630 - 14″x8½″ (35x21 cm)

Edgar Degas
VIOLINIST SEATED, STUDY, *c. 1877-78*
The Metropolitan Museum of Art, New York
5101 - 15″x11½″ (38x29 cm)

Francisco de Goya *(Spanish, 1746-1828)*
SENORA SABASA GARCIA, *c. 1814*
National Gallery of Art, Washington, D.C.
Mellon Collection
5626 - 20″x15¾″ (50x40 cm)

Franz Hals *(Dutch, 1580-1666)*
BOY WITH FLUTE
Former State Museum, Berlin-Dahlem
8719 - 24¼"x21¼" (62x54 cm)

François Boucher
MADAME BERGERET, *1746*
National Gallery of Art, Washington, D.C.
Samuel H. Kress Collection
802 - 30"x22" (76x56 cm)

Francois Clouet *(French, 1522-1572)*
PORTRAIT OF A COURT LADY, *c. 1570*
The Art Institute of Chicago
4022 - 15½"x11¼" (39x28 cm)

Francisco de Goya
DON MANUEL OSORIO DE ZUNIGA, *1784*
The Metropolitan Museum of Art, New York
The Jules S. Bache Collection
3507 - 12½"x9¼" (32x23 cm)
4400 - 14"x10¾" (35x27 cm)
715 - 30"x22¾" (76x58 cm)

Sir Thomas Lawrence
MISS MURRAY, *c. 1825-27*
The Iveagh Bequest, Kenwood, England
4528 - 14"x11" (35x28 cm)
7528 - 28"x21½" (71x54 cm)

Sir Thomas Lawrence
MASTER LAMBTON, *1824-25*
Collection of the Earl of Durham
4529 - 14"x11" (35x28 cm)

Sir Thomas Lawrence
MASTER LAMBTON *(detail)*
Collection of the Earl of Durham
4531 - 14"x11" (35x28 cm)

Sir Thomas Lawrence
PINKIE, 1794
Henry E. Huntington Library and Art Gallery, Pasadena
3141 - 11¾"x8¼" (30x21 cm)
5266 - 18"x12¾" (45x32 cm)

Thomas Gainsborough *(British, 1727-1788)*
THE BLUE BOY, *1770*
Henry E. Huntington Library and Art Gallery, Pasadena
3142 - 11¾"x8½" (30x21 cm)
5265 - 18"x13" (45x33 cm)

George Romney
MISS WILLOUGHBY, 1781-83
National Gallery of Art, Washington, D.C.
3494 - 11"x8½" (28x21 cm)

Arthur W. Devis *(British, 1763-1822)*
MASTER SIMPSON, c. 1810
Private Collection
3197 - 10"x8¼" (25x21 cm)
3337 - 11"x8½" (28x21 cm)
4337 - 14"x11¼" (35x28 cm)

Sir Joshua Reynolds *(British, 1723-1792)*
THE AGE OF INNOCENCE, *1788*
Tate Gallery, London
5201 - 20"x16½" (51x42 cm)

Sir Joshua Reynolds
LADY ELIZABETH DELME AND HER
CHILDREN, *c. 1780*
National Gallery of Art, Washington, D.C.
Mellon Collection
8260 - 30¾"x19" (78x48 cm)

Sir Joshua Reynolds
LADY BETTY HAMILTON, *1758*
National Gallery of Art, Washington, D.C.
Widener Collection
4264 - 14"x10" (35x25 cm)
5264 - 18"x12¾" (46x32 cm)
6495 - 23½"x16¾" (60x42 cm)

Sir Thomas Lawrence
LADY TEMPLETON AND HER SON, c. 1801
National Gallery of Art, Washington, D.C.
Mellon Colleciton
8259 - 31"x21½" (79x54 cm)

Sir Thomas Lawrence *(British, 1769-1830)*
THE CALMADY CHILDREN, *1823*
(Emily and Laura Anne Calmady)
The Metropolitan Museum of Art, New York
3128 - 9" circle (23 cm circle)

Edward Savage (American, *1761-1817*)
THE WASHINGTON FAMILY, 1796
National Gallery of Art, Washington, D.C.
Mellon Collection
7059 - 21"x28" (53x71 cm)

John Singleton Copley
PORTRAIT OF PAUL REVERE, *c. 1765-70*
Museum of Fine Arts, Boston
7073 - 26"x21" (66x53 cm)

Samuel F. B. Morse *(American, 1791-1872)*
GENERAL LAFAYETTE, *1826*
Brooklyn Museum, Brooklyn, N.Y.
626 - 24"x16½" (61x42 cm)

Gilbert Stuart *(American 1755-1828)*
GENERAL JOHN R. FENWICK *(Circa 1804)*
Gibbes Art Gallery, Charleston, S.C.
6463 - 24"x20" (61x51 cm)

John A. Elder *(American, 1833-1895)*
GENERAL ROBERT E. LEE, *undated*
The Corcoran Gallery of Art, Washington, D.C.
2654 - 8"x6" (20x15 cm)
3654 - 14"x10" (35x25 cm)
5654 - 20"x14½" (51x37 cm)

John A. Elder
GENERAL T. J. JACKSON, *undated*
The Corcoran Gallery of Art, Washington, D.C.
5653 - 20"x14½" (50x37 cm)

Gilbert Stuart
GEORGE WASHINGTON, *1795*
National Gallery of Art, Washington, D.C.
Mellon Collection
4443 - 14″x11″ (35x28 cm)
6443 - 24″x19″ (61x48 cm)

Gilbert Stuart
GEORGE WASHINGTON
Wadsworth Athenaeum, Hartford, Conn.
8670 - 28″x22″ (71x56 cm)

Douglas Volk *(American, 1856-1935)*
ABRAHAM LINCOLN, *1908*
National Gallery of Art, Washington, D.C.
Mellon Collection
2440 - 8″x6½″ (20x16 cm)
4440 - 14″x11″ (35x28 cm)

Rembrandt Peale *(American, 1778-1860)*
THOMAS JEFFERSON
A. D. Whiteside Collection
3435 - 9″x7½″ (23x19 cm)
5435 - 18″x15″ (46x39 cm)

George P. A. Healy *(American, 1813-1894)*
ABRAHAM LINCOLN, *1887*
National Gallery of Art, Washington, D.C.
Mellon Collection
7655 - 27½"x20" (70x51 cm)

J. Redding Kelly *(American, dates unknown)*
ABRAHAM LINCOLN
A. D. Whiteside Collection
3434 - 9"x7½" (23x19 cm)
5434 - 18"x15" (46x38 cm)

Philip Alexius de Laszlo *(Hungarian, 1869-1940)*
THEODORE ROOSEVELT, *1908*
The New York State Theodore Roosevelt Memorial
Committee of The American Museum of Natural
History, New York, 1938
6241 - 23½"x18" (60x45 cm)

Louis Lupas
JOHN F. KENNEDY, *1962*
The John F. Kennedy Collection
4140 - 13½"x10" (34x25 cm)
7140 - 28"x20¼" (71x51 cm)

RELIGIOUS ART

Albrecht Dürer,   page 66

Michelangelo Buonarroti *(Italian, 1475-1564)*
MATER DOLOROSA *(Detail from "Pieta")*
St. Peter's, Rome
5116 - 20"x16" (51x41 cm)

Michelangelo Buonarroti
PIETA, *1498-99*
St. Peter's, Rome
4096 - 14"x11" (35x28 cm)
7096 - 28"x22" (71x56 cm)

Meister des Hausbuches *(German, 1460-1490)*
THREE HOVERING ANGELS, *undated*
Kunstmuseum, Basel
4024 - 11¾"x15" (30x38 cm)

Fra Angelico (Giovanni da Fiesole) *(Italian, 1387-1455)*
THE MADONNA OF HUMILITY, *c. 1440*
National Gallery of Art, Washington, D.C.
Mellon Collection
6324 - 24¾"x18½" (63x47 cm)

Byzantine School *(XIII Century)*
ENTHRONED MADONNA AND CHILD
National Gallery of Art, Washington, D.C.
Mellon Collection
7092 - 28"x17" (71x43 cm)

Gerard David *(Flemish, 1460-1523)*
THE REST ON THE FLIGHT INTO EGYPT, *c. 1510*
National Gallery of Art, Washington, D.C.
Mellon Collection
5253 - 18″x18″ (45x45 cm)

Sandro Botticelli
MADONNA AND CHILD WITH ANGELS, *c. 1465*
National Gallery of Art, Washington, D.C.
Samuel H. Kress Collection
8045 - 30½″x20½″ (77x52 cm)

Leonardo da Vinci
THE VIRGIN AND CHILD WITH ST. ANNE
AND JOHN THE BAPTIST, *c. 1499*
National Gallery, London
7331 - 29¾″x22″ (75x56 cm)

Jusepe de Ribera *(Spanish, 1588-1652)*
MADONNA AND CHILD, *1648, dated 1626*
Philadelphia Museum of Art
William L. Elkins Collection
6841 - 24″x20″ (60x50 cm)

Giovanni Battista Moroni *(Italian, 1525-1578)*
A GENTLEMAN IN ADORATION BEFORE THE MADONNA, *c. 1560*
National Gallery of Art, Washington, D.C.
Samuel H. Kress Collection
623 - 20″x21¾″ (51x55 cm)

Nicolas Poussin
THE ASSUMPTION OF THE VIRGIN, *1626-27*
National Gallery of Art, Washington, D.C.
Gift of Mrs. Mellon Bruce
7476 - 26″x18¾″ (66x47 cm)

Giovanni Bellini
MADONNA AND CHILD IN A LANDSCAPE, *c. 1500*
National Gallery of Art, Washington, D.C.
Samuel H. Kress Collection
6497 - 24″x18½″ (61x47 cm)

Raphael
SISTINE MADONNA, *1515-1519*
Staatliche Gemäldesammlungen, Dresden
5222 - 21″x15½″ (53x39 cm)
6091 - 24″x17¾″ (61x45 cm)

Raphael
MADONNA DEL GRANDUCA, *1504-05*
Pitti Palace, Florence
3090 - 10″x5¾″ (25x14 cm)
6737 - 24″x13¾″ (61x35 cm)

Lorenzo Lotto *(Italian, 1480-1556)*
THE NATIVITY, *1523*
National Gallery of Art, Washington, D.C.
Samuel H. Kress Collection
5491 - 17¾″x13½″ (45x34 cm)

RELIGIOUS 65

Albrecht Dürer *(German, 1471-1528)*
PRAYING HANDS, *1508-09*
Albertina, Vienna
2049 - 6½″x4½″ (16x11 cm)
4049 - 11½″x8″ (29x20 cm)

Rembrandt
HEAD OF CHRIST
Staatliche Museen, Preussischer Kulturbesitz
Gemaldegalerie Berlin (West)
3247 - 10″x8″ (25x20 cm)

Sir Joshua Reynolds
THE INFANT SAMUEL AT PRAYER, *1777*
National Gallery, London
3144 - 10″x8″ (25x20 cm)
4338 - 14″x10″ (35x25 cm)
6852 - 24″x19¾″ (61x50 cm)

Titian (Tiziano Vecellio) *(Italian, 1477-1576)*
THE TRIBUTE MONEY, *1514*
Staatliche Gemäldesammlungen, Dresden
5225 - 18½″x13¾″ (47x35 cm)
7089 - 26″x19½″ (66x49 cm)

Masaccio (Tommaso Guido) *(Italian, 1401-1428)*
THE TRIBUTE MONEY *(detail), c. 1425*
Brancacci Chapel, Florence
6085 - 15"x22" (38x56 cm)

Pietro Perugino *(Italian, 1446-1523)*
THE CRUCIFIXION WITH
THE VIRGIN AND ST. JOHN, *c. 1485*
National Gallery of Art, Washington, D.C.
Mellon Collection
6719 - 24"x13" (61x33 cm)

Hans Memling
MADONNA AND CHILD WITH ANGELS, *c. 1480*
National Gallery of Art, Washington, D.C.
Mellon Collection
5251 - 20"x16" (50x40 cm)

Cornelis Massys *(Flemish, 1508-1575)*
THE ARRIVAL IN BETHLEHEM, 1543
The Metropolitan Museum of Art, New York
7832 - 21″x29½″ (53x75 cm)

Alessandro Magnasco *(Italian, 1677-1749)*
THE BAPTISM OF CHRIST, *c. 1740*
National Gallery of Art, Washington, D.C.
Samuel H. Kress Collection
747 - 24″x30″ (61x76 cm)

Stefano di Giovanni Sassetta *(Italian, c. 1392-1450)*
SAINT ANTHONY LEAVING HIS MONASTERY, *c. 1440*
National Gallery of Art, Washington, D.C.
Samuel H. Kress Collection
5117 - 18½″x13¾″ (47x35 cm)

El Greco
THE APOSTLES PETER AND PAUL, *1614*
Hermitage State Museum, Leningrad
7048 - 26"x22" (66x56 cm)

Marc Chagall
RABBI WITH TORAH, *c. 1930*
Stedelijk Museum, Amsterdam
6292 - 23½"x18" (60x45 cm)

Matthias Grünewald (German, 1475/80-1528)
THE CRUCIFIXION, *1505-10*
National Gallery of Art, Washington, D.C.
Samuel H. Kress Collection
7260 - 24"x18" (61x45 cm)

After: Leonardo da Vinci *(Italian, 1452-1519)*
THE LAST SUPPER, *1497*
Santa Maria delle Grazie, Milan
5737 - 10¼″x20″ (26x50 cm)
7737 - 15½″x30″ (39x76 cm)
9737 - 20¾″x40″ (52x101 cm)

Heinrich Hofmann, *(German, 1824-1911)*
CHRIST AT THIRTY THREE
(Detail from "Christ and the Rich Young Ruler")
The Riverside Church, New York
5718 - 20″x16″ (50x40 cm)

Heinrich Hofmann
CHRIST IN THE GARDEN OF GETHSEMANE
The Riverside Church, New York
5719 - 20″x14½″ (51x36 cm)
6716 - 24″x17½″ (61x44 cm)

Mihály Munkácsy (Hungarian, 1844-1900)
THE SAVIOUR, 1880
Museum of Fine Arts, Budapest
4671 - 14″x10¼″ (35x26 cm)
6671 - 24″x17¾″ (61x45 cm)
8671 - 31¾″x23½″ (80x59 cm)

Domenico Feti (Italian, 1589-1624)
THE VEIL OF VERONICA, c. 1613-21
National Gallery of Art, Washington, D.C.
Samuel H. Kress Collection
5396 - 24″x19¾″ (61x50 cm)

Léon Augustin L'Hermitte
HEAD OF CHRIST *(Detail from "Supper at Emmaus")*
Museum of Fine Arts, Boston
3150 - 10″x8″ (25x20 cm)
5150 - 20″x16″ (51x40 cm)

Bernhard Plockhorst *(German, 1825-1907)*
JESUS BLESSING THE CHILDREN
3132 - 10½″x7½″ (26x19 cm)

Bernhard Plockhorst
THE GOOD SHEPHERD
3130 - 10″x7″ (25x17 cm)

Endre Komaromi-Kacz *(Hungarian, 1880-1948)*
CHRIST AND THE LITTLE CHILDREN, *1917*
National Gallery, Budapest
4004 - 9¾″x14″ (24x35 cm)

Lauren Ford *(American, 1891-1973)*
THE GUARDIAN ANGEL
3192 - 11¾″x9¼″ (30x23 cm)
7192 - 26″x19½″ (66x49 cm)

Toby Edward Rosenthal *(American, 1848-1917)*
HIS MADONNA, *1908*
California Palace of the Legion of Honor, San Francisco
4842 - 13½″x10½″ (34x26 cm)
6842 - 24½″x19″ (62x48 cm)

George Hitchcock *(American, 1850-1913)*
THE FLIGHT INTO EGYPT
Private Collection
9015 - 24″x36″ (61x91 cm)

Roberto Ferruzzi *(Italian, 1853-1934)*
MADONNINA
3166 - 10″x7¾″ (25x19 cm)

Alfred Soord *(English, 1869-1915)*
THE LOST SHEEP
5391 - 20″x12½″ (51x31 cm)

Karl Hermann Fritz von Uhde *(German, 1848-1911)*
HIS OMNIPRESENCE
6720 - 18¾″x23½″ (47x59 cm)

Henry Lerolle *(French, 1848-1929)*
THE ARRIVAL OF THE SHEPHERDS
3133 - 8½″x10½″ (21x26 cm)

3044 - KING DAVID
Collection of Mr. and Mrs. James S. Plaut

3042 - MAIMONIDES, *1952*
Collection of Mr. Sidney P. Lipkins

3045 - YEHUDAH, *1955*
Collection of Mr. Kurt Delbanco

JACK LEVINE
(American, 1915-
Plate Size 10"x8"
(25x20 cm)

Series: 3041-46

3041 - KING SAUL, *1952*
Collection of Dr. Abram Kanof

3043 - KING ASA, *1953*
Fogg Art Museum, Harvard University
Meta and Paul J. Sachs Collection

3046 - HILLEL, *1955*
Collection of Mr. Nate Spingold

Hieronymus Bosch *(Flemish, 1460-1516)*
THE GARDEN OF DELIGHTS, c. 1480
Prado Museum, Madrid
9910 - three panels on one sheet
    23½"x41¾" (59x106 cm)

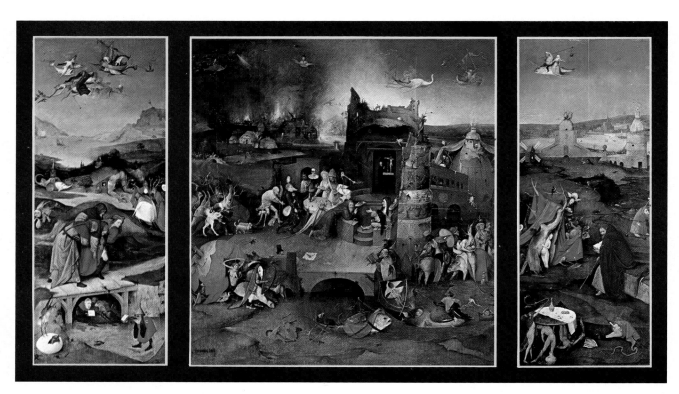

Hieronymus Bosch
THE TEMPTATION OF SAINT ANTHONY, c. 1500
Museu Nacional de Arte Antiga, Lisbon
9054 - three panels on one sheet
    24"x42" (60x106 cm)

Salvador Dalí
CRUCIFIXION (Corpus Hypercubus), 1954
The Metropolitan Museum of Art, New York
Chester Dale Collection
4691 - 14″x9″ (35x23 cm)
7691 - 28″x17¾″ (71x45 cm)

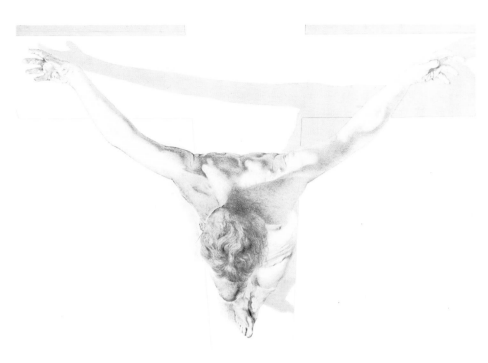

Salvador Dalí (Spanish, 1904-)
DRAWING FOR "CHRIST OF ST. JOHN
OF THE CROSS," 1950
Collection of Mr. and Mrs. A. Reynolds Morse
4666 - 11½″x14″ (29x35 cm)
7666 - 21″x28″ (53x71 cm)

lvador Dalí
IE SACRAMENT OF THE LAST SUPPER, 1955
tional Gallery of Art, Washington, D.C., Chester Dale Collection
23 - 18¾″x29¾″ (47x75 cm)
23 - 27¾″x44″ (70x112 cm)

Salvador Dalí
CHRIST OF ST. JOHN OF THE CROSS, 1951
The Glasgow Art Gallery
126 - 14″x8″ (35x20 cm)
7963999 - 28″x15½″ (71x39 cm)
(For sale in U.S. and Canada only)

GROUPS
and
FIGURES

Jan Verhas,   page 91

Jean François Millet
PLANTING POTATOES
Shaw Collection, Museum of Fine Arts, Boston
6509 - 20″x24⅜″ (51x61½ cm)

Jean François Millet *(French, 1814-1875)*
THE GLEANERS, *1857*
Louvre Museum, Paris
4498 - 10½″x14″ (26x35 cm)
6498 - 17½″x23½″ (44x59 cm)

Jean Francois Millet
THE ANGELUS, *1859*
Louvre Museum, Paris
4499 - 11″x14″ (28x35 cm)
6499 - 20″x24″ (50x60 cm)

Léon Augustin L'Hermitte *(French, 1844-1925)*
THE HAYMAKING
Private Collection
7925 - 18½"x24¾" (47x62 cm)

Jules Breton *(French, 1827-1906)*
THE SONG OF THE LARK, *1884*
The Art Institute of Chicago
Henry Field Memorial Collection
4190 - 14½"x11" (36x28 cm)

Jean-Baptiste Camille Corot
THE GYPSY GIRL AT THE FOUNTAIN, *1865-70*
Philadelphia Museum of Art
George W. Elkins Collection
3847 - 10¼"x7½" (26x19 cm)
5847 - 20"x15" (50x38 cm)

François Boucher *(French, 1703-1770)*
SPRING, *1755*
The Frick Collection, New York
497 - 10½"x14" (28x35 cm)
697 - 16¼"x21" (41x53 cm)

François Boucher
SUMMER, *1755*
The Frick Collection, New York
499 - 10½"x14" (28x35 cm)
699 - 16¼"x21" (41x53 cm)

François Boucher
AUTUMN, *1755*
The Frick Collection, New York
496 - 10½"x14" (28x35 cm)
696 - 16¼"x21" (41x53 cm)

François Boucher
WINTER, *1755*
The Frick Collection, New York
498 - 10½"x14" (28x35 cm)
698 - 16¼"x21" (41x53 cm)

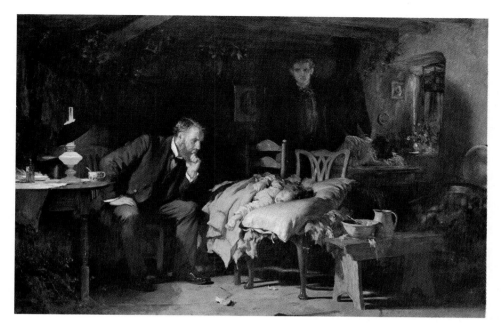

Luke S. Fildes *(British, 1844-1927)*
THE DOCTOR
Tate Gallery, London
7525 - 17½"x26" (44x66 cm)

François Boucher
THE SLEEPING SHEPHERDESS, *1750*
The Metropolitan Museum of Art, New York
The Jules S. Bache Collection
7292 - 28"x25¼" (71x64 cm)

Adolf von Menzel *(German, 1815-1905)*
THE ROUND TABLE, *1850*
National Gallery, Berlin
6930 - 24"x20¼" (61x51 cm)

John Quincy Adams *(Austrian, 1874-1933)*
HER FIRST RECITAL
4301 - 11"x13" (28x33 cm)

Bernard Pothast
THE FIRST FITTING
Private Collection
5536 - 14½"x12⅝" (37x32 cm)
7033 - 26"x23" (66x58 cm)

Bernard Pothast *(Dutch, 1882-   )*
HER FIRST LESSON
Fort Worth Art Center
5537 - 11¼"x14½" (29x37 cm)
7026 - 21"x25½" (53x65 cm)

Richard C. Woodville *(American, 1825-1855)*
THE FIRST STEP, *1847*
The New-York Historical Society
7542 - 25″x27½″ (64x70 cm)

Jacob Ochtervelt *(Dutch, c. 1635-1710)*
THE MUSICIANS, *c. 1670*
The Art Institute of Chicago
7745 - 24¾″x20″ (63x51 cm)

Pieter de Hooch
A DUTCH COURTYARD, *c. 1660*
National Gallery of Art, Washington, D.C.
Mellon Collection
536 - 19½″x16¾″ (49x42 cm)

Orazio Gentileschi
YOUNG WOMAN WITH A VIOLIN, *1612*
The Detroit Institute of Arts
7875 - 23½"x28" (59x71 cm)

Orazio Gentileschi *(Italian, 1565-1638)*
THE LUTE PLAYER, *c. 1626*
National Gallery of Art, Washington, D.C.
Gift of Mrs. Mellon Bruce
7395 - 26"x23¼" (66x59 cm)

Jean-Baptiste Greuze (French, 1725-1805)
THE WOOL WINDER, 1758-59
The Frick Collection, New York
542 - 20¼"x16½" (51x41 cm)

James McNeill Whistler
THE WHITE GIRL, 1862
National Gallery of Art, Washington, D.C.
Harris Whittemore Collection
624 - 24"x12" (61x30 cm)

Bartolomé Esteban Murillo (Spanish, 1617-1682)
A GIRL AND HER DUENNA, c. 1670
National Gallery of Art, Washington, D.C.
Widener Collection
780 - 29"x24¼" (73x61 cm)

Jean Louis Forain *(French, 1852-1931)*
COURT SCENE: INTERIOR, *undated*
The Corcoran Gallery of Art, Washington, D.C.
6341 - 20"x24" (50x61 cm)

Pierre Outin *(French, 1840-1899)*
THE TOAST
7498 - 27¾"x22¾" (70x57 cm)

Velázquez
THE SURRENDER OF BREDA, *c. 1647*
Prado Museum, Madrid
5240 - 15"x18" (38x45 cm)

Honoré Daumier (French, 1808-1879)
THE THIRD-CLASS CARRIAGE, 1860
The Metropolitan Museum of Art, New York
The H.O. Havemeyer Collection
6007 - 16"x22" (40x55 cm)

Honoré Daumier
PASSERS-BY IN FRONT OF A PRINT SHOP, c. 1860
Collection of Mr. and Mrs. Leigh B. Block
4073 - 13"x9½" (33x24 cm)

Honoré Daumier
THREE LAWYERS, undated
The Phillips Collection, Washington, D.C.
478 - 15½"x12¼" (39x31 cm)

Douglas Volk (American, 1856-1935)
LITTLE MARION (Little Maid in White), c. 1889
National Academy of Design, New York
5678 - 14¾"x15½" (37x39 cm)

Paul Chabas (French, 1869-1937)
SEPTEMBER MORN, c. 1912
The Metropolitan Museum of Art, New York
4728 - 11"x14½" (28x37 cm)
7728 - 21"x28" (52x71 cm)

Jan C. Verhas *(Belgian, 1834-1896)*
THE BROKEN FLOWER POT, *1876*
The Bruce Museum, Greenwich, CT
Gift of George Norris Morgan
8163 - 30"x20" (76x50¾ cm)

Daniel Ridgeway Knight *(American, 1839-1924)*
AN IDLE MOMENT

See Poster Section No. 30172, Page 512

Daniel Ridgeway Knight *(American, 1839-1924)*
BRITTANY GIRL
The Bruce Museum, Greenwich, CT
Gift of George N. Morgan
6278 - 22"x18" (56x45¾ cm)

Armando Miravalls Bove
FLAMENCO, 1962
Private Collection
7659 - 16½"x30" (42x76 cm)

George Bellows
GRAMERCY PARK, 1920
Private Collection
6079 - 18"x24" (45x60 cm)

George Bellows
LADY JEAN, 1924
Yale University Art Gallery
5075 - 19"x9¼" (48x23 cm)

Willem Maris *(Dutch, 1844-1910)*
CHILDREN ON A BEACH, *1876*
Wilmot E. Forbes Collection
6864 - 17"x25½" (43x64 cm)

Eugène Louis Boudin
THE BEACH AT VILLERVILLE, *1864*
National Gallery of Art, Washington, D.C.
Chester Dale Collection
9289 - 17¾"x30" (45x76 cm)

Rosa Bonheur *(French, 1822-1899)*
THE HORSE FAIR, *1853-5*
The Metropolitan Museum of Art, New York
178   - 5¼"x11" (14x28 cm)
9014 - 17"x36" (43x91 cm)

Walter Firle *(German, 1859-1929)*
THE FAIRY TALE
4702 - 11″x14″ (28x35 cm)
6702 - 18″x24″ (46x61 cm)

James Wells Champney *(American, 1843-1903)*
BOON COMPANIONS, *1879*
Smith College Museum of Art
6388 - 17″x21″ (43x53 cm)

W. V. Kaulbach *(German, 1805-1874)*
GRETEL
2999 - 7½″x6″ (19x15 cm)
3999 - 12″x9″ (30x23 cm)

HANSEL
2998 - 7½″x6″ (19x15 cm)
3998 - 12″x9″ (30x23 cm)

Emile Renouf *(French, 1845-1894)*
THE HELPING HAND, *1881*
The Corcoran Gallery of Art
Washington, D.C.
4638 - 11″x14″ (28x35 cm)
8638 - 22″x32″ (56x81 cm)

Diego Rivera
FLOWER VENDOR, *1935*
San Francisco Museum of Art
7555 - 28″x28″ (71x71 cm)

Diego Rivera
OAXACA
Brooklyn Museum, Brooklyn, N.Y.
4782 - 10½″x15½″ (26x39 cm)

Diego Rivera
MOTHER'S HELPER, *1950*
Private Collection
5788 - 13½″x18″ (33x46 cm)

Wolfgang Hutter *(Austrian, 1928-)*
THE LOVERS, *1950*
7328 - 18½″x26″ (47x66 cm)

Robert Vickrey *(American, 1926-)*
CARRIE AND COCOA, *1970 (detail)*
Private Collection
8848 - 22″x32″ (55x81 cm)

James Ensor *(Belgian, 1860-1949)*
CARNIVAL, *c. 1920*
Stedelijk Museum, Amsterdam
7750 - 20½"x28" (52x71 cm)

Ben Shahn
BROTHERS
Joseph H. Hirshhorn Museum, Washington, D.C.
6067 - 25¾"x17" (66x43 cm)

Willem De Kooning *(Dutch, 1904-   )*
QUEEN OF HEARTS, *1943-46*
The Joseph H. Hirshhorn Foundation
7720 - 31¾"x19" (80x48 cm)

Robert A. Heindel *(Contemporary American)*
CORPS DES ENFANTS, *1980*
Collection of Mr. and Mrs. John B. Hipp
8129 - 20½"x29¾" (52x75 ½cm)

Stephen Hustvedt *(American, 1925-   )*
I REMEMBER—IT WAS MARCH . . .
Private Collection
9055 - 22"x36" (56x91 cm)

Huldah
HIS ROSE
2835 - 7½″x6″ (19x15 cm)
5835 - 20″x16″ (50x40 cm)

Huldah
PRINTEMPS
5752 - 19¾″x6¼″ (50x16 cm)

Huldah
MOIS DE MAI
5753 - 19¾″x6¼″ (50x16 cm)

Huldah *(Contemporary American)*
IN CENTRAL PARK
4806 - 14″x11″ (35x28 cm)
6909 - 25″x20″ (63x51 cm)

Huldah
MAY BUD
2836 - 7½″x6″ (19x15 cm)
4836 - 14″x11″ (35x28 cm)
5836 - 20″x16″ (50x40 cm)

Huldah
TAVERN-ON-THE-GREEN
4805 - 14″x11″ (35x28 cm)
6908 - 25″x20″ (63x51 cm)

Huldah
PREMIERE AU RENDEZ-VOUS
4778 - 14″x11″ (35x28 cm)

Huldah
BIG BROTHER
5834 - 20″x16″ (50x40 cm)

Huldah
LITTLE SISTER
5833 - 20″x16″ (50x40 cm)

James Chapin
BOY WITH A GLOBE, *1927-28*
Collection of the Artist
7339 - 21½″x26″ (54x66 cm)

James Chapin
BOY WITH A BOOK, *1945*
Private Collection
6062 - 21″x18″ (54x45 cm)

James Chapin
THE PICTURE BOOK, *1945-46*
Private Collection
5340 - 16½″x11″ (42x28 cm)

GROUPS & FIGURES   103

James Chapin *(American, 1887-1975)*
RUBY GREEN SINGING, *1928*
Norton Gallery and School of Art
West Palm Beach, Florida
6868 - 27¾"x22" (70x55 cm)

Robert Brackman *(American, 1896-   )*
STUDY: MORNING INTERLUDE
5279 - 20"x15" (51x38 cm)

James Chapin *(American, 1887-1975)*
MOTHERHOOD
Private Collection
6049 - 21½"x17½" (54x45 cm)

Guy Bardone
FLOWER MARKET
Private Collection
9665 - 25½″x41″ (65x104 cm)

Harrison Rucker *(American, 1930-)*
THE PINK GOWN
Private Collection
6525 - 24″x18″ (61x46 cm)

Sheldon Clyde Schoneberg
ANGEL OF BLEEKER STREET, 1967
Private Collection
4992 - 17″x13¼″ (43x33 cm)
8273 - 34″x25″ (86x63 cm)

Sheldon Clyde Schoneberg
DEBORAH DREAMING, 1970
Private Collection
4995 - 17″x13¼″ (43x33 cm)
8960 - 40″x30″ (101x76 cm)

Sheldon Clyde Schoneberg
DIANE, 1969
Private Collection
4994 - 17″x13¼″ (43x33 cm)
8969 - 30″x25½″ (76x64 cm)

Sheldon Clyde Schoneberg *(American, 1926-   )*
TAMBOURINES, 1968
Private Collection
4993 - 13¼″x17″ (33x43 cm)
8525 - 27¼″x36″ (69x91 cm)

IMPRESSIONISM

Pierre August Renoir,   page 131

Paul Cézanne
VASE OF FLOWERS, *1874*
Durand-Ruel Collection, New York
630 - 20½″x16½″ (52x42 cm)

Paul Cézanne
HOUSES ON THE HILL, *1900-06*
Marion Koogler McNay Art Institute, San Antonio, Texas
8965 - 23″x30″ (58x76 cm)

Paul Cezanne (French, 1839-1906)
ROCKS IN THE PARK OF CHATEAU NOIR, 1900
The Fine Arts Museums of San Francisco
Mildred Anna Williams Fund
7028 - 22"x30" (56x76 cm)

Paul Cézanne
HOUSE OF PERE LACROIX, 1873
National Gallery of Art, Washington, D.C.
Chester Dale Collection
6823 - 24"x19½" (61x50 cm)

Paul Cézanne
THE RED ROCK, 1895-99
Musée de l'Orangerie, Paris
7575 - 28"x20½" (71x52 cm)

Edgar Degas
THE BALLET CLASS, *c. 1880*
Philadelphia Museum of Art
7843 - 27½"x26" (71x66 cm)

Edgar Degas
LA DANSEUSE AU BOUQUET, *1878*
Rhode Island School of Design
Museum of Art, Providence
4837 - 11"x14" (27x35 cm)

Edgar Degas
FOUR DANCERS, *c. 1899*
National Gallery of Art, Washington, D.C.
Chester Dale Collection
4017 - 11"x14" (28x35 cm)

Edgar Degas
DANCERS IN THE WINGS, *c. 1890*
The Art Institute of Chicago
5727 - 17"x13" (43x33 cm)

Edgar Degas
BEFORE THE BALLET *(detail), 1888*
National Gallery of Art, Washington, D.C.
Widener Collection
4019 - 11"x14" (28x35 cm)

Paul Gauguin
FATATA TE MITI, 1892
National Gallery of Art, Washington, D.C.
Chester Dale Collection
4256 - 11"x14" (27x35 cm)

Henri de Toulouse-Lautrec
MAXIME DETHOMAS, 1896
National Gallery of Art, Washington, D.C.
Chester Dale Collection
4345 - 14"x11" (35x28 cm)

Henri de Toulouse-Lautrec *(French, 1864-1901)*
DANSEUSE, *undated*
Stedelijk Museum, Amsterdam
W.O. Koenigs Collection
6295 - 23"x18½" (58x47 cm)

Paul Gauguin
TWO TAHITIAN WOMEN WITH MANGOES, *1899*
The Metropolitan Museum of Art, New York
4602 - 14″x11¼″ (35x29 cm)
660   - 23″x18″ (59x45 cm)

Paul Gauguin *(French, 1848-1903)*
TAHITIAN MOUNTAINS, *1891-93*
The Minneapolis Institute of Arts
5290 - 14½″x20″ (37x50 cm)

Vincent van Gogh
A SIDEWALK CAFE AT NIGHT, *1888*
Rijksmuseum Kröller-Müller, Holland
5543 - 14½"x11" (37x28 cm)
5428 - 20"x15½" (50x40 cm)

Vincent van Gogh *(Dutch, 1853-1890)*
STARLIGHT OVER THE RHONE, *1888*
Collection of Mr. F. Moch, Paris
7387 - 20"x25" (50x63 cm)

Vincent van Gogh
THE BRIDGE, *1888*
Rijksmuseum Kröller-Müller, Holland
5542 - 11½″x14½″ (29x37 cm)

Vincent van Gogh
THE DRAWBRIDGE AT ARLES, *1888*
Private Collection
5288 - 15″x15″ (38x38 cm)

Vincent van Gogh
VEGETABLE GARDENS, *1888*
Stedelijk Museum, Amsterdam
Collection of V.W. van Gogh
5287 - 16"x20" (40x51 cm)

Vincent van Gogh
STILL LIFE WITH ONIONS, *1889*
Rijksmuseum Kröller-Müller, Holland
4320 - 12"x16" (30x40 cm)

Vincent van Gogh
STREET IN AUVERS, *1890*
Athenaeum, Gallery of Art, Helsinki
5873 - 16"x20" (40x50 cm)

Vincent van Gogh
STILL LIFE WITH GLOVES, *1889*
Private Collection
4319 - 12"x16" (30x40 cm)

Vincent van Gogh
PORTRAIT OF ARMAND ROULIN, *1888*
Folkwang Museum, Essen
5283 - 20"x16" (50x40 cm)

Vincent van Gogh
BOATS OF SAINTES-MARIES, *1888*
Stedelijk Museum, Amsterdam
Collection of V.W. van Gogh
5541 - 11½"x14½" (29x37 cm)
5284 - 16"x20" (41x51 cm)

Vincent van Gogh
THE POSTMAN ROULIN, 1888
Museum of Fine Arts, Boston
7074 - 28″x22″ (71x56 cm)

Vincent van Gogh
ZOUAVE, 1888
Stedelijk Museum, Amsterdam
Collection of V.W. van Gogh
4321 - 14½″x12″ (37x30 cm)

Vincent van Gogh
LA BERCEUSE, 1889
The Art Institute of Chicago
5867 - 20½″x16″ (52x40 cm)

Vincent van Gogh
SUNFLOWERS WITH YELLOW BACKGROUND, *1888*
Stedelijk Museum, Amsterdam
Collection of V.W. van Gogh
5540 - 14½"x10¾" (37x27 cm)
6385 - 20½"x15½" (52x39 cm)

Vincent van Gogh
PINK AND WHITE ROSES, *1890*
Private Collection
5286 - 16"x20" (41x50 cm)

Vincent van Gogh
SUNFLOWERS, *1888*
Philadelphia Museum of Art
5544 - 14½"x11¼" (37x29 cm)
6386 - 20½"x16" (52x40 cm)
756 - 30"x23½" (76x59 cm)

Edouard Manet (French, 1832-1883)
GARE SAINT-LAZARE, 1873
National Gallery of Art, Washington, D.C.
Gift of Horace Havemeyer in memory
of his mother Louisine W. Havemeyer
7081 - 22½″x28″ (57x71 cm)

Edouard Manet
GUITAR AND SOMBRERO
Calvet Museum, Avignon
7810 - 17½″x28″ (45x71 cm)

Claude Monet
BASSIN D'ARGENTEUIL, c. 1874
Rhode Island School of Design
Museum of Art, Providence
7836 - 22"x29½" (55x75 cm)

Claude Monet
THE HOUSES OF PARLIAMENT, SUNSET, *1903*
National Gallery of Art, Washington, D.C.
Chester Dale Collection
8282 - 29"x33" (74x84 cm)

Claude Monet
THE RED BOATS, *1875*
Private Collection
5523 - 13″x18″ (33x46 cm)
817 - 22″x30″ (56x76 cm)

Claude Monet
ARGENTEUIL, *c. 1875*
Musée de l'Orangerie, Paris
7573 - 21¾″x25½″ (55x64 cm)

Claude Monet *(French, 1840-1926)*
WILLOWS OF VETHEUIL
The Corcoran Gallery of Art
Bequest of Edward C. and Mary Walker
8135 - 24½"x30" (62¼x76 cm)

Claude Monet
BANKS OF THE SEINE, VETHEUIL, 1880
National Gallery of Art, Washington, D.C.
Chester Dale Collection
775 - 22"x30" (55x77 cm)

Claude Monet
WATER LILIES *(detail, left side), 1914-18*
Musée de l'Orangerie, Paris
8268 - 12½"x30" (32x76 cm)

Claude Monet
WHITE AND PURPLE WATER LILIES, *1918*
Larry Aldrich Collection, New York
9809 - 27"x36" (68x91 cm)

Claude Monet
WATER LILIES *(detail, right side), 1914-18*
Musée de l'Orangerie, Paris
8269 - 12½"x30" (32x76 cm)

Claude Monet
THE SEINE AT GIVERNY, MORNING MISTS

See Poster Section No. 30201, Page 507

Claude Monet
GLADIOLI

See Poster Section No. 30204, Page 507

Claude Monet *(French, 1840-1926)*
WATERLILIES AND JAPANESE BRIDGE, *1899*
The Art Museum, Princeton University
7632 - 28″x28″ (71x71 cm)

Claude Monet
JARDIN DE GIVERNY, *1917*
Musée de Grenoble
8966 - 36″x27¼″ (91x69 cm)

Claude Monet *(French, 1840-1926)*
STILL LIFE, c. *1876*
Gulbenkian Collection
718 - 20″x28″ (51x71 cm)

Claude Monet
SUNFLOWERS, *1881*
The Metropolitan Museum of Art, New York
The H.O. Havemeyer Collection, 1929
7284 - 30″x24″ (76x61 cm)

Claude Monet
SPRING FLOWERS, *1864*
The Cleveland Museum of Art
Gift of Hanna Fund
8285 - 32″x24½″ (81x62 cm)

Pierre Auguste Renoir
THE ESTEREL MOUNTAINS
The Corcoran Gallery of Art, Washington, D.C.
7499 - 22⅝"x28" (57½x71 cm)

Pierre Auguste Renoir
LE PONT DES ARTS, c. 1868
The Norton Simon Foundation
9302 - 24"x40" (61x101 cm)

Pierre Auguste Renoir
LUNCHEON OF THE BOATING PARTY, *1881*
The Phillips Collection, Washington, D.C.
5531 - 13¼″x18″ (34x46 cm)
7735 - 20½″x28″ (52x71 cm)

Pierre Auguste Renoir
THE SEINE AT ARGENTEUIL

See Poster Section No. 30200, Page 506

Pierre Auguste Renoir
OARSMEN AT CHATOU, *1879*
National Gallery of Art, Washington, D.C.
901 - 28¾″x35½″ (73x90 cm)

Pierre Auguste Renoir
CHILD IN WHITE, (detail), c. 1883
The Art Institute of Chicago
4444 - 16"x12½" (40x31 cm)

Pierre Auguste Renoir
MADEMOISELLE LACAUX, 1864
Cleveland Museum of Art
6777 - 22"x17½" (55x44 cm)

Pierre Auguste Renoir
PORTRAIT OF LUCIE BERARD
Private Collection
4077 - 15¼"x11¼" (39x28 cm)

Pierre Auguste Renoir
ROSE AND BLUE, *1881*
Museum of Art, São Paulo
4445 - 14"x9" (35x22 cm)

Pierre Auguste Renoir
A GIRL WITH A WATERING CAN, *1876*
National Gallery of Art, Washington, D.C.
Chester Dale Collection
4020 - 14"x11" (35x28 cm)
6099 - 22"x16" (55x41 cm)

Pierre Auguste Renoir
GABRIELLE AND JEAN, *1895*
Musée de l'Orangerie, Paris
7571 - 25½"x21¼" (65x54 cm)

Pierre Auguste Renoir
LADY WITH A MUFF, *undated*
The Metropolitan Museum of Art, New York
5794 - 15"x10½" (39x26 cm)

Pierre Auguste Renoir
ON THE TERRACE, *1881*
The Art Institute of Chicago
5532 - 18"x14" (46x35 cm)
7684 - 27½"x22" (70x56 cm)

Pierre Auguste Renoir
BAL A BOUGIVAL, *1883*
Museum of Fine Arts, Boston
885 - 32"x17" (81x43 cm)

Pierre Auguste Renoir
TWO GIRLS AT THE PIANO, *c. 1883*
Joslyn Art Museum, Omaha, Nebraska
4603 - 14″x11½″ (35x29 cm)
6322 - 21¾″x18″ (55x46 cm)

Pierre Auguste Renoir
LADY AT THE PIANO, *c. 1875*
The Art Institute of Chicago
4334 - 14″x11″ (36x29 cm)

Pierre Auguste Renoir
PORTRAIT OF A YOUNG GIRL, *1884*
Private Collection
4078 - 15″x12″ (38x30 cm)

Pierre Auguste Renoir
WOMAN WITH LILACS, *1877*
Private Collection
603 - 22¾"x18¼" (58x46 cm)

Pierre Auguste Renoir *(French, 1841-1919)*
LA SOURCE, *1910*
Art Associates Partnership
Hamilton, Bermuda
7714 - 30"x24" (76x61 cm)

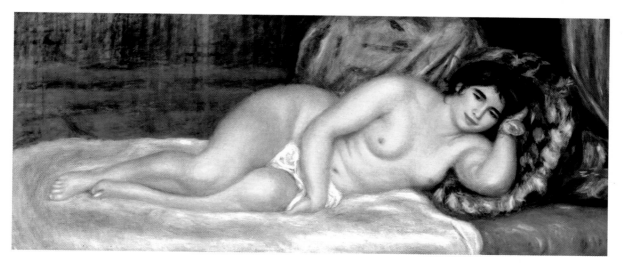

Pierre Auguste Renoir
THE NUDE GABRIELLE, *1908*
Musée de l'Orangerie, Paris
9574 - 15″x36″ (38x91 cm)

Pierre Auguste Renoir
YOUNG BATHER, *1892*
Private Collection
4076 - 15″x11¾″ (38x30 cm)

Pierre Auguste Renoir
LITTLE NUDE IN BLUE, *1880*
Albright-Knox Art Gallery, Buffalo
4075 - 15½″x12″ (39x30 cm)
5778 - 20″x16″ (50x40 cm)

Pierre Auguste Renoir
BOUQUET DANS UN VASE, *c. 1878*
Indianapolis Museum of Art
The Lockton Collection
5065 - 20¼″x14″ (51x35 cm)

Pierre Auguste Renoir
ROSES, *1879*
Private Collection
547 - 20½″x17″ (52x43 cm)

Georges Seurat
A SUNDAY AFTERNOON ON THE
ISLAND OF LA GRANDE JATTE, *1884-86*
The Art Institute of Chicago
7734 - 19″x28″ (48x71 cm)

Georges Seurat *(French, 1859-1891)*
THE SIDE SHOW, *1889*
The Stephen C. Clark Collection, New York
7051 - 22″x33¼″ (56x84 cm)

Georges Seurat
PORT EN BESSIN: THE OUTER HARBOR (LOW TIDE)

See Poster Section No. 30206, Page 505

Georges Seurat
LADY WITH A MUFF, *c. 1884*
The Art Institute of Chicago
3084 - 12″x9¼″ (30x23 cm)

Alfred Sisley *(French, 1839-1899)*
THE ROAD AT LOUVECIENNES, *1875*
Musée de l'Orangerie, Paris
6399 - 18″x24″ (45x61 cm)

Aristide Maillol *(French, 1861-1944)*
HEAD OF A YOUNG GIRL
Musée Rigaud, Perpignan
6850 - 17¼″x24″ (44x61 cm)

Camille Pissarro
BORDS DE L'EAU A PONTOISE, *1872*
Mrs. Norton Simon, Los Angeles
8265 - 21¾"x35¾" (55x91 cm)

John Singer Sargent *(American, 1856-1925)*
OYSTER GATHERERS OF CANCALE, *1878*
The Corcoran Gallery of Art, Washington, D.C.
8279 - 21¾"x34" (55x86 cm)

Mary Cassatt
SLEEPY BABY

See Poster Section No. 30179,
Page 507

Mary Cassatt *(American, 1845-1926)*
WOMEN ADMIRING A CHILD, *undated*
Detroit Institute of Arts
7565 - 22¾″x28″ (58x71 cm)

Mary Cassatt
AFTER THE BATH, *1901*
The Cleveland Museum of Art
6775 - 16½″x26″ (42x66 cm)

Louis C. Tiffany *(American, 1848-1933)*
AT IRVINGTON-ON-HUDSON
Nelle Cochrane Woods Collection, Nebraska Art Association,
Courtesy of the Sheldon Memorial Art Gallery, Lincoln
6393 - 18"x24" (45x60 cm)

Maurice Prendergast *(American, 1859-1924)*
CENTRAL PARK, *1901*
Whitney Museum of American Art, New York
6675 - 14"x21½" (36x55 cm)

Frank W. Benson *(American, 1862-1951)*
PORTRAIT OF MY DAUGHTERS
Worcester Art Museum
6056 - 20¼"x28" (51x71 cm)

Frank Weston Benson
EVENING LIGHT

See Poster Section No. 30187,
Page 509

William Merritt Chase
NEAR THE BEACH, SHINNECOCK

See Poster Section No. 30196, Page 509

William M. Chase *(American, 1849-1916)*
CHRYSANTHEMUMS, *c. 1878*
National Gallery of Art, Washington, D.C.
Chester Dale Collection
9288 - 21¾"x36" (55x91 cm)

George Wharton Edwards *(American, 1869-1950)*
THE OLD RIVER ROAD
The Bruce Museum, Greenwich, CT
8166 - 23¼"x28" (59x71 cm)

Willard Leroy Metcalf *(American, 1858-1925)*
GLOUCESTER HARBOUR
Mead Art Museum, Amherst College, Amherst, MA
8157 - 24¼"x27" (61½x68½ cm)

William Chadwick
IRISES

See Poster Section No. 30208, Page 508

William Chadwick *(American, 1879-1962)*
HAMBURG COVE
The Holyoke Museum, Holyoke, Mass.
8160 - 24"x26½" (61x67¼ cm)

Winslow Homer
THE FOUR LEAF CLOVER

See Poster Section No. 30203, Page 510

Winslow Homer
CROSSING THE PASTURE

See Poster Section No. 30207,
Page 510

Winslow Homer
THE HUDSON RIVER—LOGGING

See Poster Section No. 30191, Page 510

Charles Ebert
FISHERMAN'S HUT

See Poster Section No. 30205, Page 508

Frederick Carl Frieseke
THE GARDEN PARASOL

See Poster Section No. 30202, Page 508

Childe Hassam
RAINY DAY, BOSTON

See Poster Section No. 30197, Page 511

Childe Hassam
FLAGS ON THE FRIAR'S CLUB

See Poster Section No. 30209, Page 511

Childe Hassam
RIALTO MARKET, VENICE

See Poster Section No. 30198, Page 511

Daniel Garber *(American, 1880-1958)*
CHERRY BLOSSOMS, *1914*
Private Collection
7031 - 21"x21" (53½x53½ cm)

Childe Hassam *(American, 1859-1935)*
THE GARDEN DOOR, *c. 1888*
Courtesy Berry-Hill Galleries, Inc., New York
7822 - 19¾"x16¼" (50x41¼ cm)

Rae Sloan Bredin *(American, 1881-1933)*
THE ARTIST'S FAMILY ON A PARK BENCH
Private Collection
6967 - 24"x29" (61x73½ cm)

Robert Henry Logan *(American, 1874-1942)*
THE YELLOW HOUSE, *1908*
From the Collection 9,
The Artists Guild and Gallery, Charlestown, R.I.
6392 - 20"x24" (50x61 cm)

Edward Henry Potthast *(American, 1857-1927)*
CHILDREN BY THE SEA
Hirshhorn Museum and Sculpture Garden,
Smithsonian Institution
4271 - 12"x16" (30x41 cm)

Gustave Caillebotte
PERISSOIRES SUR L'YERRES

See Poster Section No. 30171, Page 506

John H. Twachtman
SPRINGTIME

See Poster Section No. 30185,
Page 506

Gari Melchers (*American, 1860-1932*)
UNPRETENTIOUS GARDEN
Telfair Academy of the Arts and Sciences, Savannah, Ga.
6968 - 24″x28¾″ (61x73 cm)

William J. Glackens
THE DREAM RIDE
Private Collection
5081 - 15"x17" (38x43 cm)

William J. Glackens *(American, 1870-1938)*
THE BEACH AT ANNISQUAM
Private Collection
5005 - 16½"x20" (42x50 cm)

Edmund C. Tarbell
THREE SISTERS—A STUDY IN JUNE SUNLIGHT 1890
Collection of the Milwaukee Art Museum
Gift of Mrs. Montgomery Sears
8146 - 25"x29" (63½x73½ cm)

Joseph DeCamp *(American, 1858-1923)*
RED ROOFS
Private Collection
8158 - 28"x22½" (71x57½ cm)

Traditional and Contemporary
LANDSCAPES

Nancy Taylor Stonington,   page 195

Thomas Gainsborough *(British, 1727-1788)*
THE MARKET CART
Tate Gallery, London
6444 - 25¼"x21" (64x53 cm)

Thomas Gainsborough
VIEW NEAR KING'S BROMLEY-ON-TRENT, STAFFORDSHIRE, *1770-74*
Philadelphia Museum of Art
William L. Elkins Collection
9848 - 25½"x35¾" (65x91 cm)

John Constable *(British, 1776-1837)*
THE WHITE HORSE, *1819*
The Frick Collection, New York
5527 - 12¾"x18" (32x46 cm)
730 - 18"x26" (45x66 cm)
929 - 25"x36" (63x91 cm)

John Constable
THE HAY WAIN, *1821*
National Gallery, London
5211 - 12½"x18¼" (32x46 cm)

John Constable
WIVENHOE PARK, ESSEX, *1816*
National Gallery of Art, Washington, D.C.
Widener Collection
9258 - 19½"x36" (49x91 cm)

William Shayer *(English, Early 19th Century)*
FIGURES OUTSIDE AN INN
5528 - 17¼"x14½" (44x37 cm)
7916 - 28"x23" (71x58 cm)

Colin Hunter, *(British, 1841/42-1904)*
A SAWMILL ON THE RIVER SNAKE, *1889*
Private Collection
9652 - 40"x30" (101x76 cm)

Alfred Parsons
BREDON-ON-THE-AVON, 1913 (detail)
The Corcoran Gallery of Art, Washington, D.C.
5524 - 17¼"x14½" (44x37 cm)

Alfred Parsons *(British, 1847-1920)*
BREDON-ON-THE-AVON, 1913
The Corcoran Gallery of Art, Washington, D.C.
6245 - 16"x24" (40x60 cm)
9278 - 24"x36" (61x91 cm)

Jacob I. van Ruisdael *(Dutch, 1628-1682)*
WHEATFIELDS, *undated*
The Metropolitan Museum of Art, New York
738 - 22¾"x29¾" (58x75 cm)

Jacob I. van Ruisdael
LANDSCAPE WITH A FOOTBRIDGE, *1652*
The Frick Collection, New York
900 - 23¾"x36½" (60x93 cm)

Aelbert Cuyp *(Dutch, 1620-1691)*
THE VALKHOF AT NIJMEGEN, *c. 1656-60*
Indianapolis Museum of Art
7986 - 20¼"x30½" (51x77 cm)

Meindert Hobbema
A VIEW ON A HIGH ROAD, *1665*
National Gallery of Art, Washington, D.C.
Mellon Collection
967 - 25¾″x35¾″ (65x91 cm)

Jan van der Heyden *(Dutch, 1637-1712)*
SQUARE IN UTRECHT, *1670*
Mr. Norton Simon, Los Angeles
6348 - 17½″x23½″ (44x60 cm)

Hendrick Goltzius *(Dutch, 1558-1616)*
GROUP OF TREES IN A WOOD
Kunsthalle, Hamburg
3248 - 11″x8″ (27x20 cm)

Canaletto
THE QUAY OF THE PIAZZETTA, *c. 1740*
National Gallery of Art, Washington, D.C.
Gift of Mrs. Barbara Hutton
990 - 26¾"x36" (68x91 cm)

Canaletto
THE SQUARE OF ST. MARK, *c. 1740*
National Gallery of Art, Washington, D.C.
Gift of Mrs. Barbara Hutton
489 - 10¼"x14" (26x35 cm)

Canaletto
PORTICO WITH LANTERN, c. 1745
The Art Institute of Chicago
Gift of Mrs. Clive Runnels
6094 - 18¾"x22¾" (47x58 cm)

Canaletto
THE TERRACE, c. 1745
The Art Institute of Chicago
Gift of Mrs. Clive Runnels
6095 - 18¾"x22¾" (47x58 cm)

Francesco Guardi *(Italian, 1712-1793)*
FANTASTIC LANDSCAPE, c. 1760
(From the Castello di Colloredo, Udine)
The Metropolitan Museum of Art, New York
9088 - 15½"x40" (39x100 cm)

Bernardo Bellotto
THE CASTLE OF NYMPHENBURG, *1761*
National Gallery of Art, Washington, D.C.
Samuel H. Kress Collection
9090 - 20½"x35¾" (52x91 cm)

Canaletto
THE PORTELLO AND THE BRENTA CANAL AT PADUA, c. 1735-40
National Gallery of Art, Washington, D.C.
Samuel H. Kress Collection
9087 - 22¾"x40" (57x101 cm)

Giovanni Paolo Panini *(Italian, 1692-1764)*
VIEW OF THE ROMAN FORUM, 1747
The Walters Art Gallery, Baltimore
9541 - 24½"x40" (62x101 cm)

Jean-Jacques dit John Chalon *(Swiss, 1778-1854)*
LA FORGE DE LA CORRATERIE, *1829*
Musée d'Art et d'Histoire, Genéve
6813 - 26"x20" (65x51 cm)

Karl Heffner *(German, 1849-1925)*
MOON GLOW
Private Collection
6018 - 17"x28" (43x71 cm)

Adolf Friedrich Harper *(German, 1725-1806)*
ITALIAN LANDSCAPE, *1799*
National-Galerie, Berlin
9650 - 25½″x40″ (64x101 cm)

Johann Martin von Rohden
(German, 1778-1868)
MIDDAY, *1829*
Staatliche Kunstsammlungen Kassel
Neue Galerie
8107 - 24″x33½″ (61x85 cm)

Hubert Robert
THE OBELISK, *1787*
The Art Institute of Chicago
4460 - 14"x12" (35x30 cm)
7460 - 28"x24¼" (71x61 cm)

Hubert Robert
THE LANDING, *1788*
The Art Institute of Chicago
4461 - 14"x12" (35x30 cm)
7461 - 28"x24¼" (71x61 cm)

Hubert Robert
THE FOUNTAINS, *1787-88*
The Art Institute of Chicago
4259 - 14"x12" (35x30 cm)
7259 - 28"x24¼" (71x61 cm)

Hubert Robert
OLD TEMPLE, *1787*
The Art Institute of Chicago
4258 - 14"x12" (35x30 cm)
7258 - 28"x24¼" (71x61 cm)

Hubert Robert
THE TERRACE, *1794*
The Baltimore Museum of Art
4270 - 14″x10″ (35x25 cm)

Hubert Robert
THE ROMAN GARDEN, *1794*
The Baltimore Museum of Art
4269 - 14″x10″ (35x25 cm)
7269 - 28″x20″ (71x50 cm)

Hubert Robert
THE OLD BRIDGE, c. *1775*
National Gallery of Art, Washington, D.C.
Samuel H. Kress Collection
902 - 26¾″x35¾″ (68x91 cm)

J. R. Hervé
MOUNTAIN IDYLL
Private Collection
8298 - 25¼"x32" (64x81 cm)

Hubert Robert *(French, 1733-1808)*
TERRACE OF THE CHATEAU DE MARLY, *c. 1777*
Nelson Gallery and Atkins Museum, Kansas City, Missouri
9045 - 24½"x36" (62x91 cm)

Jean-Honoré Fragonard
THE GOOD MOTHER
3139 - 11¾"x10" (30x25 cm)

Jean-Honoré Fragonard
OATH OF LOVE
3140 - 12"x10" (30x25 cm)

Jean-Honoré Fragonard *(French, 1732-1806)*
A GAME OF HOT COCKLES, *1767-73*
National Gallery of Art, Washington, D.C.
Samuel H. Kress Collection
4929 - 14"x10¾" (35x27 cm)

Jean-Honoré Fragonard
A GAME OF HORSE AND RIDER, *1767-73*
National Gallery of Art, Washington, D.C.
Samuel H. Kress Collection
4928 - 14"x10¾" (35x27 cm)

Jean-Baptiste Camille Corot
THE FOREST OF COUBRON, *1872*
(Le Retour au Logis)
National Gallery of Art, Washington, D.C.
Widener Collection
7255 - 29½"x24" (75x61 cm)

Henri Joseph Harpignies
LANDSCAPE AT SUNDOWN *(detail), 1897*
Private Collection
8967 - 36"x28" (91x71 cm)

Jean-Baptiste Camille Corot *(French, 1796-1875)*
LAGO DI GARDA
Private Collection on loan to the
San Diego Museum of Art
6037 - 26"x20½" (66x52 cm)

Jean-Baptiste Camille Corot
SITE D'ITALIE, *1839*
The Norton Simon Collection
8283 - 21″x32″ (53x81 cm)

Jean-Baptiste Camille Corot
THE BRIDGE OF NARNI, *1865-70*
National Gallery of Canada, Ottawa
666 - 16″x24″ (40x61 cm)
966 - 25½″x35¾″ (64x91 cm)

Henri Joseph Harpignies *(French, 1819-1916)*
A FARMHOUSE, *undated*
The Norton Simon Foundation, Los Angeles
4074 - 10½"x16" (26x40 cm)

Jean-Baptiste Camille Corot
LE LAC DE TERNI, *1861*
The Corcoran Gallery of Art
Washington, D.C.
4221 - 10¾"x16" (27x40 cm)
9663 - 24"x35¾" (61x91 cm)

Jean-Baptiste Camille Corot
LANDSCAPE NEAR GENEVA, *1841*
Museum of Art and History, Geneva
5257 - 12½"x18" (31x45 cm)

Jean-Baptiste Camille Corot *(French, 1796-1875)*
VILLE D'AVRAY, *c.1867-70*
National Gallery of Art, Washington, D.C.
Gift of Count Cecil Pecci-Blunt
5529 - 13½"x18" (34x46 cm)
7058 - 19"x25" (48x63 cm)

Jean-Baptiste Camille Corot
REMEMBRANCE OF TERRACINA, *1864*
The Corcoran Gallery of Art, Washington, D.C.
W.A. Clark Collection
4222 - 10¾"x13½" (27x34 cm)
8024 - 25½"x31½" (65x80 cm)

Pierre Bonnard
VUE CANNES, *1931*
Collection of Mr. and Mrs. David Lloyd Kreeger
7512 - 16¼"x30" (41x76 cm)

Tivadar Csontváry Kosztka *(Hungarian, 1853-1919)*
DRIVE AT NEW MOON IN ATHENS, *1904*
Private Collection
5361 - 24"x18¼" (61x46 cm)

El Greco
VIEW OF TOLEDO, *1609*
The Metropolitan Museum of Art, New York
The H.O. Havemeyer Collection
769 - 28"x24¾" (71x63 cm)

George Inness
THE LACKAWANNA VALLEY, *1855*
National Gallery of Art
Washington, D.C.
Gift of Mrs. Huttleston Rogers
9011 - 24¼"x36" (61x91 cm)

George Inness
A PASSING SHOWER
Private Collection
5078 - 12"x19" (31x48 cm)

George Inness
PEACE AND PLENTY, *1865*
The Metropolitan Museum of Art, New York
7608 - 20½"x30" (52x76 cm)

LANDSCAPES 179

Thomas Moran (*American, 1837-1926*)
SEEKING NEW HUNTING GROUNDS
Kimball Art Foundation, Fort Worth, Texas
9061 - 19"x36" (48x91 cm)

Thomas Moran
GRAND CANYON OF THE YELLOWSTONE,
WYOMING, *1906*
Private Collection
8674 - 20"x30" (51x76 cm)

Albert Bierstadt *(American, 1830-1902)*
ESTES PARK
Denver Public Library
9060 - 21″x36″ (53x91 cm)

Albert Bierstadt
LOOKING UP THE YOSEMITE VALLEY
Pioneer Museum & Haggin Galleries
9979 - 22¼″x36″ (56x91 cm)

William T. Richards *(American, 1833-1905)*
IN THE ADIRONDACK MOUNTAINS
St. Louis Art Museum
9063 - 24″x32″ (61x81 cm)

Thomas Hill *(American, 1829-1908)*
MILL CREEK CANYON
E. B. Crocker Art Gallery
Sacramento, California
9659 - 22″x38″ (56x96 cm)

Jasper F. Cropsey *(American, 1823-1900)*
MOUNTAIN LAKES, *1871*
Private Collection
9851 - 24″x36″ (61x91 cm)

William Sonntag *(American, 1822-1900)*
MOUNTAIN LAKE NEAR PIEDMONT, MARYLAND, *1860*
National Collection of Fine Arts
Smithsonian Institution, Washington, D.C.
9299 - 25¾″x40″ (65x101 cm)

Willard L. Metcalf *(American, 1858-1925)*
THE LAST SNOW
Private Collection
7960 - 26¾"x30" (68x76 cm)

Frederick J. Waugh
MOUNTAIN LANDSCAPE
Edwin A. Ulrich Museum of Art
Wichita State University
8110 - 20½"x30" (52x76 cm)

Paul Wenck (American, 1892-   )
ROCKIES FROM BEAR LAKE
(Rocky Mountain National Park)
9859 - 27"x36" (68x91 cm)

Gene Pelham
VALLEY STREAM
6566 - 17"x21" (43x53 cm)

William Keith
SAN FRANCISCO SHORELINE
Private Collection
9057 - 24"x36" (61x91 cm)

Ralph Albert Blakelock *(American, 1847-1919)*
INDIAN ENCAMPMENT
The University of Arizona, Museum of Art,
Gift of Raymond Burr
7540 - 22"x30" (56x76 cm)

George Inness *(American, 1825-1894)*
THE WOOD CHOPPER, *1849*
The Cleveland Museum of Art
Mr. and Mrs. William H. Marlatt Fund
6325 - 20"x24" (50x61 cm)

Asher B. Durand *(American, 1796-1886)*
MONUMENT MOUNTAIN, BERKSHIRES,
undated
Detroit Institute of the Arts
9903 - 24″x36″ (61x91 cm)

Jerome B. Thompson *(American, 1814-1886)*
THE OLD OAKEN BUCKET
7040 - 18″x28″ (45x71 cm)

Asher B. Durand
SUNDAY MORNING, *1839*
The New-York Historical Society
7644 - 17½″x26″ (45x66 cm)
9537 - 24½″x36″ (62x91 cm)

Fairfield Porter (American, 1907-1975)
VIEW OF BARRED ISLAND, 1970
The Herbert W. Plimpton Collection on extended loan
to the Rose Art Museum, Brandeis University
8115 - 24"x30" (61x76 cm)

Orris Moe (Contemporary American)
RIDE AT SUNRISE
Private Collection
8113 - 19½"x32" (49x81 cm)

Maynard Dixon *(American)*
MESAS IN SHADOWS
Collection of Brigham Young University
7539 - 22⅜″x30″ (56x76 cm)

Edgar Payne *(American, 1882-1947)*
MESA IN THE DESERT
Private Collection
8106 - 25½″x32″ (65x81 cm)

Marianne Hornbuckle *(Contemporary American)*
JEMEZ SERIES, *1981*
Collection of the Artist
9719 - 26½"x36" (67¼x91½ cm)

Marianne Hornbuckle *(Contemporary American)*
SANGRE DE CRISTO VIII, *1984*
Private Collection
9856 - 26½"x36" (67¼x91½ cm)

Marianne Hornbuckle *(Contemporary American)*
CANYON WALKS IX
Private Collection
9982 - diptych, each panel 28″x22″ (71x56 cm)

Marianne Hornbuckle *(Contemporary American)*
BIG BEND

See Poster Section No. 30132, Page 522

A. Taylor (American, 1941-   )
MARY'S MESAS, 1976
Private Collection

See Poster Section No. 30160, Page 521

A. Taylor
LINGERING BELOW
Collection of Ned and Linda Corman

See Poster Section No. 30015, Page 521

Ann Taylor (*Contemporary American*)
PRESTWICK DEPARTURE

See Poster Section No. 30184, Page 520

Ann Taylor (*Contemporary American*)
UMBER PEAKS

See Poster Section No. 30098, Page 520

Nancy Taylor Stonington *(Contemporary American)*
CHERRY BLOSSOMS, *1985*
Courtesy of GWS Galleries, Carmel, Calif.
8165 - diptych, single sheet overall 20"x32" (50¾x81 cm)

Nancy Taylor Stonington *(Contemporary American)*
MOUNTAIN LANDSCAPE, *1985*
Courtesy of The Stonington Gallery, Seattle, Wash.
8164 - diptych, each panel 30"x20" (76x50¾ cm)

Nancy Taylor Stonington (Contemporary American)
INSIDE PASSAGE, 1985
Courtesy of The Stonington Gallery, Seattle, Wash.
9989 - 22″x34″ (56x86½ cm)

Nancy Taylor Stonington (Contemporary American)
OREGON COAST, 1985
Private Collection
9988 - 22″x34″ (56x86½ cm)

Yasu Eguchi *(Japanese, 1938-   )*
COUNTERPOINT
Private Collection
7347 - 22″x30″ (55x76 cm)

Philip Aziz *(Canadian, 1923-   )*
LIFE CYCLE OF PINE TREE NO. 9, *1968*
Private Collection
9006 - 36″x24″ (91x60 cm)

A. Taylor *(American, 1941-   )*
UMBER MIST
Private Collection
9056 - 30″x30″ (76x76 cm)

Tadashi Asoma *(Japanese, 1923-)*
LILY POND IN SUMMER
Private Collection
8103 - 28″x28″ (71x71 cm)

Joan Paley *(Contemporary American)*
SPRING
Private Collection
8345 - 25″x30″ (63x76 cm)

Ray Vinella *(Contemporary American)*
THE SAND BAR, *1984*
Private Collection
7351 - 20″x24″ (50¾x61 cm)

A.B. Makk *(Contemporary American)*
SPRING, *1951*
Private Collection
8147 - 22″x27″ (56x68½ cm)

Vilnis Strazdins (Contemporary American)
MOUNTAIN TWILIGHT, 1981
Private Collection
7633 - 26½″x29¾″ (67½x75½ cm)

Sidney F. Willis (Contemporary American)
AWAKENING, 1981
Harris Peel Gallery, Danby, Vermont
8132 - 25″x32″ (64x81 cm)

Arnold Alaniz *(Contemporary American)*
SPRINGTIME, *1984*
Collection of the Artist
7861 - 24"x30" (61x76 cm)

Lee Hochberg *(Contemporary American)*
BESIDE THE STILL WATERS, *1981*
Collection of the Artist
8120 - 26½"x32" (67x81 cm)

Michael Gibbons *(Contemporary American)*
MISTY CANAL
Private Collection
6538 - 18"x18" (45¾x45¾ cm)

Michael Gibbons *(Contemporary American)*
MARGARET'S LANDING, *1985*
Private Collection
8159 - 16"x28¼" (40½x71¾ cm)

Leonard Brooks *(Contemporary Canadian)*
MORNING BEACH, BAJA, CALIFORNIA
Collection of the Artist
8128 - 24¾″x29¾″ (63x76 cm)

Frank Trefny *(Contemporary American)*
TOD'S POINT - NOVEMBER, *1980*
Private Collection
8951 - 25″x32″ (63½x81 cm)

Fred D. MacNeill *(Contemporary American)*
TIDAL FLOW
Private Collection
8131 - 24″x32″ (61x81½ cm)

Hannah Ferenbach *(Contemporary American)*
THE TRACK ROAD, *1982*
Collection of the Artist
8139 - 26½″x20¼″ (67¼x51½ cm)

Margaret Grimes *(Contemporary American)*
DWARF APPLE, *1983*
Collection of Bellevue Hospital Center
Artist Represented by Fischbach Gallery, New York
8151 - 26″x26″ (66x66 cm)

Hans Moller (American, 1905-   )
PINE LEDGE, 1979
Midtown Galleries, New York
6668 - 18″x24″ (46x61 cm)

Marlon Malcom (Contemporary American)
RUSSIAN RIVER V, 1979
The John Pence Gallery, San Francisco
8652 - 24″x32″ (61x81 cm)

Trevyh *(Contemporary French)*
GLEN MIST
Private Collection
6346 - 22″x28¼″ (56x72 cm)

Trevyh *(Contemporary French)*
BIRCH COVE
Private Collection
6345 - 26″x20″ (66x51 cm)

Trevyh *(Contemporary French)*
SEVEN BIRCHES
Private Collection
6344 - 26″x20″ (66x51 cm)

Kyohei Inukai *(Contemporary American)*
THE RED HOSE, *1981*
Collection of Mrs. Nancy Goodenow
6945 - 24″x19″ (61x48½ cm)

Nicholas Roerich *(Russian, 1874-1947)*
THE MOUNTAIN SCHITROVAYA, *1925*
The Nicholas Roerich Museum, New York
8121 - 18″x30″ (46x76 cm)

Marcella Maltais (b. Quebec, 1933-   )
HYDRA EN ROSE, *1969-1972*
Private Collection
6316 - 28″x21¼″ (71x54 cm)

Bob Peak *(Contemporary American)*
NIGHT MUSIC
Private Collection
8123 - 28″x28″ (71x71 cm)

4051 - SNUG HARBOR

4052 - POINSETTIA TERRACE

4053 - VILLAGE LANE

4054 - SUNNY MORNING

4055 - COUNTRY INN

4056 - BLUE BAY

BERMUDA SCENES
by Adolph Treidler *(Contemporary American)*
4000 Series - 10"x14" (25x35 cm)

Robert Henri *(Robert Henry Cozad)*
WEST COAST OF IRELAND, *1913*
Everson Museum of Art, Syracuse, New York
8100 - 26″x32″ (66x81 cm)

Winslow Homer
THE SHELL HEAP, *1904*
Private Collection
5780 - 18″x12½″ (45x32 cm)

Winslow Homer
HOMOSASSA RIVER, *1904*
Brooklyn Museum, New York
5779 - 18″x12½″ (45x32 cm)

Louis Berthommé-Saint-André *(French 1905-   )*
LES BORDS DU LEZ A CASTELNAU, *1964*
Private Collection
9673 - 30″x37½″ (76x95 cm)

Bernardo Sanjuan *(Spanish, 1915-   )*
OLIVE TREES, MALLORCA
Private Collection
8274 - 26″x33″ (66x83 cm)

Pierre Jaques
SWISS VILLAGE
Private Collection
9094 - 14¾"x39¼" (37x99 cm)

Dalhart Windberg *(American, 1933-   )*
BIG TREE, *1971*
Private Collection
5522 - 12"x18" (30x46 cm)
9050 - 24"x36" (60x91 cm)

Guy Bardone
LA LOIRE A CHAUMONT, *1970*
David B. Findlay Galleries, New York
7631 - 28″x22½″ (71x57 cm)

Bernard Buffet
SOMME RIVER LOCK, *1962*
Private Collection
8023 - 25½″x34″ (65x86 cm)

André Derain
THE OLD BRIDGE, *1910*
National Gallery of Art, Washington, D.C.
Chester Dale Collection
8505 - 25″x31″ (63x78 cm)

André Derain *(French, 1880-1954)*
LANDSCAPE, THE BLUE OAK
Private Collection
5289 - 16″x20″ (40x50 cm)

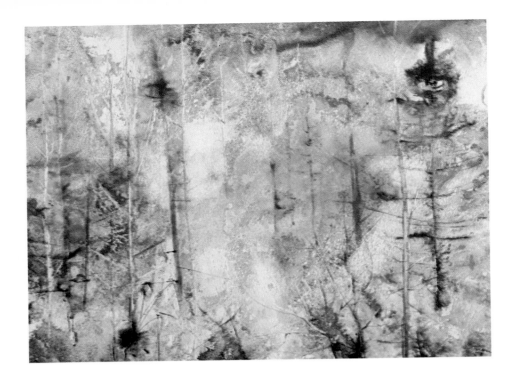

William Thon
SEPTEMBER WOODS
Private Collection
6847 - 20½″x27″ (52x69 cm)

William Thon
COASTAL AUTUMN
Private Collection
7892 - 20½″x27″ (52x68 cm)

William Thon *(American 1906-   )*
OVERGROWN QUARRY
Private Collection
7891 - 20½″x27″ (52x68 cm)

René Genis (French, 1922-   )
LUMIERE SUR LE LAC
From The Bolger Collection
8117 - 28″x28″ (71x71 cm)

Bernard Cathelin (French, 1919-   )
MORIN VALLEY IN THE SNOW, *1969*
David B. Findlay Galleries, New York
9972 - 27½″x35″ (69x88 cm)

Jane V. Chenoweth *(American, 1910-   )*
FLOWERING QUINCE, *1970*
Private Collection
5549 - 18″x14¼″ (46½x36 cm)
8959 - 28¼″x22½″ (71x57 cm)

Augustus V. Tack *(American 1870-1949)*
CANYON
The Phillips Collection, Washington, D.C.
7973 - 22″x30½″ (56x76 cm)

Marcella Maltais *(b. Quebec, 1933-)*
THROUGH LOVING EYES
Private Collection
8510 - 32"x25¼" (81x64 cm)

Dianne Nelson Tullis *(Contemporary American)*
EARLY FALL, *1970*
Collection of William F. Buckley, Jr.
9976 - 36"x26¾" (91x67 cm)

Philip Aziz
APOTHEOSIS OF A PINE TREE
Private Collection
7947 - 30"x20" (76x51 cm)

Malcolm Thompson
SANCTUARY
Private Collection
7322 - 28"x22" (71x56 cm)

Ronald Ekholm *(American, 1942-   )*
FLOWER POT
Private Collection
6445 - 19"x25" (48x63 cm)

Porfirio Salinas, Jr. *(American, 1910-   )*
BLUE BONNET TRAIL
8626 - 25½"x31½" (65x80 cm)

Porfirio Salinas, Jr.
BLUE BONNET TIME
8627 - 25½"x31½" (65x80 cm)

John Weiss *(Contemporary American)*
BRICK SHED, *1977*
Private Collection
6931 - 18"x24" (45x61 cm)

Ethel P. Margolies *(American, 1907-   )*
VERMONT BARN, *1969*
Private Collection
9970 - 18¾″x46½″ (47x118 cm)

Luigi Lucioni
ROUTE SEVEN
6053 - 16″x21″ (40x53 cm)

Luigi Lucioni
SUNLIT PATTERNS
5666 - 14″x20″ (35x50 cm)

John Wheat
SEPTEMBER HARVEST
9664 - 13½"x35¼" (34x89 cm)

Georges Schreiber *(American, 1904-1977)*
IN TENNESSEE
Private Collection
4061 - 12"x16" (30x40 cm)

Georges Schreiber
HAYING
Private Collection
4062 - 12"x16" (30x40 cm)

Gary Barsumian *(Armenian, 1923-1978)*
THE NEIGHBORS
Collection of Mrs. Gary Barsumian
9071 - 18"x36" (45x91 cm)

Rockwell Kent *(American, 1882-1971)*
WINTER, A VIEW OF MONHEGAN, MAINE, *1907*
The Metropolitan Museum of Art, New York
6830 - 16½"x22" (42x56 cm)

John Steuart Curry *(American, 1897-1946)*
THE LINE STORM, *1934*
Private Collection
6055 - 15½″x24″ (40x61 cm)

John Steuart Curry
WISCONSIN LANDSCAPE
The Metropolitan Museum of Art
9905 - 17½″x35¼″ (44x89 cm)

Herbert Lucas *(American, 1941-)*
AWAITING SPRING, *1975*
Private Collection
8547 - 24″x30″ (61x76 cm)

Dean Fausett *(Contemporary American)*
COLORADO RANCH
Private Collection
9110 - 23¾″x38¾″ (60x98 cm)

Howard Connolly
DUCKS LANDING
Private Collection
7622 - 22¼″x28¼″ (56x71 cm)

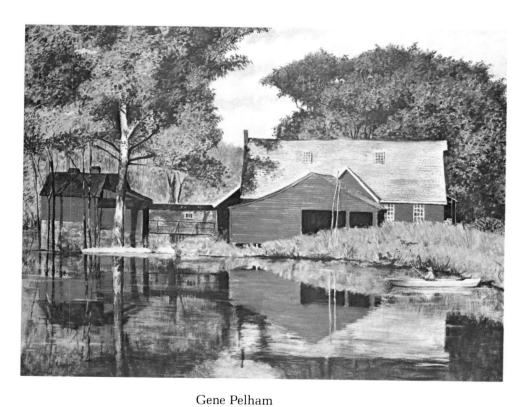

Gene Pelham
PEACEFUL WATERS
3534 - 9″x12″ (23x30 cm)
6534 - 17″x21″ (43x53 cm)
8534 - 25″x31″ (63x79 cm)

Scarlett *(Contemporary American)*
CORN SNOW, *1968*
Collection of Albert G. Chase
4646 - 11½″x16″ (29x40 cm)

Scarlett
HARBINGER, *1971*
Private Collection
4647 - 11½″x16″ (29x40 cm)

Series: 4646-49

Scarlett
REBIRTH, *1971*
Private Collection
4649 - 11½″x16″ (29x40 cm)

Scarlett
LOW BRANCH, *1968*
Collection of Albert G. Chase
4648 - 11½″x16″ (29x40 cm)

Charles Sheeler (American, 1883-1965)
BUCKS COUNTY BARN, 1923
Whitney Museum of American Art, New York
6677 - 18½"x24" (47x60 cm)

Patsy Santo (American, 1893-1975)
WINTER STILLNESS
Estate of the Artist
7792 - 22"x30" (56x76 cm)

SEASCAPES
and
BOATING SCENES

W. Lee Hankey, page 239

Willem van de Velde *(Dutch, 1633-1707)*
FISHING BOATS OFFSHORE IN A CALM
Museum of Fine Arts, Springfield, Mass.
8862 - 26¼"x32" (66x81 cm)

R.B. Spencer *(English, 19th Century)*
LEAVING PORT
Collection of Robert Baskowitz, Jr.
8398 - 16¾"x30" (42x76 cm)

Thomas Moran *(American, 1837-1926)*
SPLENDOR OF VENICE, *1889*
Philbrook Art Center, Tulsa
8948 - 25¾"x30" (65½x76 cm)

Joseph Mallord William Turner
EAST COWES CASTLE, THE SEAT OF J. NASH, ESQ.
THE REGATTA BEATING TO WINDWARD, *1828*
Indianapolis Museum of Art
8105 - 24"x32" (61x81 cm)

Joseph M.W. Turner
THE DOGANA AND SANTA MARIA
DELLA SALUTE, VENICE, *c. 1843*
National Gallery of Art, Washington, D.C.
5507 - 11¼"x18" (29x46 cm)
9838 - 23"x36" (58x91 cm)

Joseph M.W. Turner
THE GRAND CANAL, VENICE, *1839*
The Metropolitan Museum of Art, New York
9837 - 29½"x39¼" (75x100 cm)

Alfred Thompson Bricher *(American, 1837-1908)*
SUNSET CAPE ELIZABETH, MAINE, *1878*
Indianapolis Museum of Art, Martha Delzell Memorial Fund
9973 - 18¾"x37¾" (47x95 cm)

Jack Wilkinson Smith *(American, 1873-1949)*
ROCKY SHORE
Wilmot E. Forbes Collection
9304 - 27"x36" (68x91 cm)

Johan Jongkind *(Dutch, 1819-1891)*
THE RIVER MEUSE, *1866*
Havre Museum
5310 - 14¼"x20" (36x51 cm)

James Bard *(American, 1815-1897)*
THE ALIDA, *1848*
The New-York Historical Society
8364 - 18"x32" (46x81 cm)

Fitz Hugh Lane *(American, 1804-1865)*
BOSTON HARBOR, *1853*
The Bostonian Society, Boston, Massachusetts
7240 - 20"x30¾" (51x78 cm)

J. G. Evans *(American, 19th century)*
THE SHIP ST. MARY'S ENTERING HARBOR AT MOBILE
Hirschl and Adler Galleries
5501 - 14¼"x18" (36x46 cm)
7959 - 24"x30" (61x76 cm)

Charles Robert Patterson *(American, 1878-1958)*
THE "HENRY B. HYDE"
Collection of Columbian Rope Company
Auburn, N.Y.
8856 - 24"x32" (61x81 cm)

James Sessions *(American, 1882-1962)*
ROUNDING THE HORN
Private Collection
6865 - 20"x25" (50x63 cm)

William James Aylward
(American, 1875-1956)
U.S.S. "CONSTITUTION"
8678 - 24"x32" (61x81 cm)

Gustave Courbet
BEACH AT ETRETAT, *c. 1869*
National Gallery of Art, Washington, D.C.
Chester Dale Collection
9284 - 24¼″x36″ (61x91 cm)

Jean-Baptiste Camille Corot
QUAI DES PAQUIS, GENEVA, *1841*
Museum of Art and History, Geneva
5256 - 12½″x18″ (31x45 cm)

Jean-Baptiste Camille Corot
HOUSES AT HONFLEUR, *1830*
Private Collection
7007 - 17½″x25¼″ (44x64 cm)

William Keith *(American, 1839-1911)*
CYPRESS POINT, *1890*
William Keith Memorial Art Gallery
Oakland Art Museum
7010 - 11¼″x26″ (28x66 cm)
9010 - 17″x40″ (43x101 cm)

W. Lee Hankey *(British, 1869-1952)*
FISHERMAN'S COVE
8639 - 26″x31″ (66x79 cm)

Raymond Wintz *(French, 1884-1956)*
FISHING BOATS
6492 - 21½″x17½″ (55x44 cm)

Raymond Wintz
THE BLUE DOOR
7999 - 30″x24″ (76x61 cm)

James M. Sessions
FISHERMAN'S WHARF
Private Collection
7561 - 22″x28″ (56x71 cm)

James M. Sessions
READY TO SAIL
Private Collection
7563 - 22″x28″ (56x71 cm)

Winslow Homer
THE SLOOP - BERMUDA, *1899*
The Metropolitan Museum of Art, New York
5103 - 13½″x19½″ (34x49 cm)

Winslow Homer
STOWING THE SAIL, BAHAMAS, *1903*
The Art Institute of Chicago
5818 - 14″x21½″ (35x54 cm)

Winslow Homer
THE GULF STREAM, *1899*
The Art Institute of Chicago
5820 - 11"x20" (28x51 cm)

Winslow Homer
NORTHEASTER, *1895*
The Metropolitan Museum of Art, New York
9829 - 25½"x37½" (65x95 cm)

Winslow Homer
THE HERRING NET, *1885*
The Art Institute of Chicago
7827 - 18½"x30" (47x76 cm)

Winslow Homer
BREEZING UP, *1876*
National Gallery of Art, Washington, D.C.
Mellon Collection
5509 - 11¼"x18" (29x46 cm)
833 - 19½"x31" (49x78 cm)

Edward Hopper *(American, 1882-1967)*
THE GROUND SWELL, *1939*

See Poster Section, No. 30190, Page 505

Paule Stetson Loring *(American, 1899-1968)*
A GLOUCESTER SWORDFISHERMAN
Private Collection
7815 - 22″x30″ (55x76 cm)

Robert Wesley Amick *(American, 1879-1969)*
THE BOUNDING MAIN
7139 - 22½″x30″ (57x76 cm)

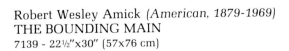

James Sessions
MISTY MORNING
5510 - 13½″x18″ (34x46 cm)
7063 - 20″x26½″ (51x67 cm)

James Sessions
OUTWARD BOUND
5511 - 13½″x18″ (34x46 cm)
7062 - 20″x26½″ (51x67 cm)

James Sessions
A GOOD BREEZE
7064 - 20″x26½″ (51x67 cm)

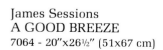

SEASCAPES & BOATING SCENES 245

Louis Rosan *(French, 1926-   )*
LITTLE HARBOR IN BRITTANY
Private Collection
7224 - 21″x28½″ (53x72 cm)

Louis Rosan
LA ROCHELLE
Private Collection
7225 - 21″x28½″ (53x72 cm)

Bernard Buffet
HARBOR IN BRITTANY, *1965*
Private Collection
7335 - 19″x25″ (48x63 cm)

James McNeill Whistler
BATTERSEA REACH, c. 1865
The Corcoran Gallery of Art, Washington, D.C.
Bequest of James Parmelee
8288 - 20″x30″ (50x76 cm)

Charles Sheeler
PERTAINING TO YACHTS AND YACHTING, 1922
Philadelphia Museum of Art
6259 - 20″x24″ (50x60 cm)

John Lutes
JERRY JIMMY
Private Collection
7390 - 24″x30″ (60x76 cm)

John Atwater *(Contemporary American)*
JOHN'S BAY, *1984*
Collection of Nicki Nichols Gamble
7288 - 19½″x20¼″ (49½x51½ cm)

John D. Lutes
EBB TIDE
Private Collection
7971 - 22″x30″ (56x76 cm)

Vern Broe (Contemporary American)
THE DORY
Private Collection
7919 - 15¼"x30" (39x76 cm)

Emil Carlsen (American, 1853-1932)
THE SOUTH STRAND
National Collection of Fine Arts
Smithsonian Institution
7957 - 25"x28" (63x71 cm)

John Lutes (American, 1926-   )
THREE DORIES
Artists Guild and Gallery, Charlestown, R.I.
5502 - 18"x14¼" (46x36 cm)
8859 - 30"x24" (76x61 cm)

Pierre Doutreleau *(Contemporary French)*
THE GREAT HARBOR, *1982*
Private Collection
8137 - 25″x36″ (63½x91½ cm)

Pierre Doutreleau *(Contemporary French)*
DISTANT HARBOR
Private Collection
7233 - 20½″x30″ (52x76 cm)

Pierre Doutreleau *(Contemporary French)*
LA PLAGE, *1985*
Private Collection
7500 - 21¾"x30" (55¼x76 cm)

Pierre Doutreleau *(Contemporary French)*
AFTER THE STORM
Private Collection
8343 - 28"x28" (71x71 cm)

Dan Poole *(Contemporary American)*
TO THE SEA
Private Collection
6686 - 20″x26½″ (50¾x67¼ cm)

Dan Poole *(Contemporary American)*
SEACASTLE
Private Collection
8167 - 20″x25½″ (50¾x64¾ cm)

Dan Poole *(Contemporary American)*
SUNRISE REGATTA BEACH, *1980*
Collection of the Artist
8140 - 20″x30″ (50¾x76 cm)

Dan Poole *(Contemporary American)*
RAINBOW BEACH, *1977*
Collection of Dr. John C. Bess
8116 - 26¼″x30″ (66x76 cm)

Pierre Doutreleau
THE WAVE
Private Collection
7914 - 17½"x30½" (44x66 cm)

Robert Maione *(Contemporary American)*
CLIFFS AND SURF, CALIFORNIA, *1977*
The John Pence Gallery, San Francisco
9072 - 24"x36¼" (61x92 cm)

Philip Jamison
ISLAND SHORE
Hirschl and Adler Galleries, New York
7345 - 21⅜"x30" (54x76 cm)

Fred D. MacNeill *(Contemporary American)*
SHORE PATTERNS
Private Collection
8130 - 25½"x28" (64½x71 cm)

Fred D. MacNeill *(Contemporary American)*
FAR END
Private Collection
9074 - 20"x36½" (51x93 cm)

Raymond de Botton
PAINTING NO. 1: GREEK ISLAND, *1966*
Collection of Mr. and Mrs. Nathan Cummings
9636 - 24″x40″ (61x101 cm)

Noel Richards *(Contemporary Jamaican)*
NIGRIL BEACH, *1982*
Private Collection
8142 - 19¾″x26½″ (50x67¼ cm)

Raymond de Botton *(Spanish, 1925-   )*
THE BLUE SAIL
Private Collection
8952 - 25½″x32¼″ (64x82 cm)

Raymond de Botton *(Spanish, 1925-   )*
LA MER A CARREAUX, *1967*
Collection of William F. Buckley, Jr., New York
9658 - 28¼″x36″ (71x91 cm)

Walter Andrews *(American, 1907-1969)*
BREAKING SURF, *1939 (detail)*
7693 - 16"x30" (40x76 cm)

Walter Andrews
BLUE GULF STREAM *(detail)*
7854 - 16"x30" (40x76 cm)

Frederick J. Waugh
POUNDING SURF
Edwin A. Ulrich Gallery, Hyde Park, N.Y.
4311 - 11″x14″ (28x35 cm)
6787 - 17″x21″ (43x53 cm)
7787 - 22″x28″ (56x71 cm)

Frederick J. Waugh *(American, 1861-1940)*
OPEN SEA
9535 - 27″x36″ (68x91 cm)

Frank K. M. Rehn, N.A. *(American, 1848-1914)*
IN THE GLITTERING MOONLIGHT, undated
The Corcoran Gallery of Art, Washington, D.C.
9654 - 24″x36″ (61x91 cm)

Suzy Aalund
WINDSWEPT DUNES
Private Collection
8261 - 9¾"x35¾" (24x91 cm)

Suzy Aalund *(Contemporary American)*
SUMMER BREEZES
Private Collection
5512 - 14½"x14½" (37x37 cm)
7931 - 23¾"x23¾" (60x60 cm)

Suzy Aalund
SUNSWEPT DUNES
Private Collection
5513 - 11¾"x18" (30x46 cm)
9067 - 23½"x35½" (60x90 cm)

Benjamin Williams Leader
THE SANDY MARGIN OF THE SEA, *1890*
The Forbes Magazine Collection, New York
5504 - 12"x18" (30x46 cm)
9666 - 24"x36" (61x91 cm)

Dana Noble *(American, 1915-   )*
AFTERNOON AT FALMOUTH
Private Collection
7943 - 20"x30" (51x76 cm)

Malcolm Thompson *(American, 1916-   )*
A BREEZE OF DAISIES, *1978*
Collection of Mr. and Mrs. Gordon H. Anderson
7321 - 28"x24¾" (71x62 cm)

Malcolm Thompson
MORNING FLIGHT
Collection of Mr. and Mrs. Walter S. Hennig
8114 - 30"x26⅜" (76x67 cm)

Howard Connolly *(Contemporary American)*
GULLS AT SEA
Private Collection
6661 - 20¼"x24¼" (51x61 cm)

AMERICANA

Sidney F. Willis,   page 275

Copyright © 1977 by Andrew Wyeth
Andrew Wyeth
WOLF RIVERS, *1959*
Private Collection
5561 - 13¼″x12¾″ (34x32 cm)

Copyright © 1976 by Andrew Wyeth
Andrew Wyeth
GERANIUMS, *1960*
Private Collection
6115 - 20½″x15¼″ (52x39 cm)

Andrew Wyeth
EVENING AT KUERNERS, *1970*
Private Collection
7241 - 18½"x28¾" (47x73 cm)

Andrew Wyeth
THE MILL, *1959*
Private Collection
5560 - 14"x22½" (36x57 cm)

Andrew Wyeth
FLOUR MILL

See Poster Section No. 30192, Page 513

Andrew Wyeth
GROUND WIRE

See Poster Section No. 30193, Page 513

Copyright © Andrew Wyeth
Andrew Wyeth *(Contemporary American)*
LIBERTY LAUNCH
Private Collection
8171 - 20½"x28" (52x71 cm)

Copyright © Andrew Wyeth
Andrew Wyeth *(Contemporary American)*
MASTER BEDROOM
7770 - 18"x25" (45¾x63½ cm)

Andrew Wyeth *(Contemporary American)*
THE WRITING CHAIR
5233 - 20¾"x13" (53x33 cm)

Andrew Wyeth *(American, 1917-)*
FARAWAY, 1952
Private Collection
6507 - 13½"x21¼" (34x51 cm)

Andrew Wyeth
AFTER PICKING, *1942*
Private Collection
6506 - 18″x26″ (46x66 cm)

Andrew Wyeth *(Contemporary American)*
FULL MOON
5125 - 17″x22″ (43x56 cm)

James Wyeth *(Contemporary American)*
EXCURSION BOATS, MONHEGAN ISLAND
Private Collection
8168 - 21¼"x30" (54x76 cm)

James Wyeth *(Contemporary American)*
ISLAND LIBRARY
Private Collection
8170 - 20½"x28" (52x71 cm)

James Wyeth *(Contemporary American)*
ISLAND ROSES, *1968*
Private Collection
6272 - 18½"x23¾" (47x60 cm)

James Wyeth *(Contemporary American)*
THE RED HOUSE
Private Collection
8169 - 18″x27½″ (45¾x70 cm)

James Wyeth *(Contemporary American)*
LEGHORNS
Private Collection
6540 - 18″x24″ (45¾x61 cm)

AMERICANA 273

Ken Davies *(Contemporary American)*
BLUE AGGIE, *1982*
Private Collection
5345 - 14″x19″ (35½x48¼ cm)

Ken Davies
GISLER MALLARD
Private Collection
7969 - 18½″x30″ (47x77 cm)

Ken Davies *(Contemporary American)*
ANTIQUE SALE, CANADIAN GOOSE DECOY
Collection of General Mills, Inc.
5538 - 14½″x18″ (37x46 cm)
6046 - 22″x28″ (56x71 cm)

Sidney F. Willis *(Contemporary American)*
A CORNER OF MY LIFE, *1983*
Collection of Katherine Adele Gartner
Represented by The Peel Gallery, Danby, Vermont
8145 - 22½"x27¾" (57½x70½ cm)

Sidney F. Willis *(Contemporary American)*
VARIATIONS IN GRAY
Collection of Mr. and Mrs. Alex Herzen
Represented by The Peel Gallery, Danby, Vermont
8149 - 20"x30½" (50¾x77½ cm)

Ron Becker *(Contemporary American)*
TABLE WITH QUILT, *1983*
Collection of the Artist
8144 - 27¼"x22" (69¼x56 cm)

John Chumley *(Contemporary American)*
JOHN'S DOG, *1980*
Private Collection
7001 - 16¾"x21½" (42½x54½ cm)

Robert McGinnis *(Contemporary American)*
HARVEST HOME, *1983*
Private Collection
8148 - 18"x36" (45¾x91½ cm)

Pauline Campanelli *(Contemporary American)*
ALL AMERICAN
Collection of Mr. and Mrs. David Stoller
8152 - 23"x29¾" (58½x75½ cm)

Pauline Campanelli *(Contemporary American)*
SQUAW CORN, *1985*
George Miller and William Fretz
8153 - 14½"x31¾" (36½x80½ cm)

Dan Campanelli *(Contemporary American)*
UNDER THE PINES, *1985*
Mr. and Mrs. Daniel C. de Roulet
7503 - 19¾″x25¾″ (50x65½ cm)

Dan Campanelli *(Contemporary American)*
THE DAILY BEGGARS, *1985*
Collection of the Artist
8154 - 18″x27¼″ (45¾x69¼ cm)

Dan Campanelli *(Contemporary American)*
CLOSED FOR THE WINTER, *1985*
Mr. and Mrs. Irving Hochberg
8155 - 19″x26¾″ (48¼x68 cm)

Thomas William Jones *(Contemporary American)*
AUTUMN TABLE, *1984*
Collection of the Artist
7502 - 16¼"x25" (41¼x63½ cm)

Thomas William Jones *(Contemporary American)*
PACKARD'S AT CHRISTMAS, *1978*
Bellevue Art Museum, Bellevue, WA
6995 - 17¼"x24" (44x61 cm)

Thomas William Jones *(Contemporary American)*
ELEVEN POINTER, *1985*
Private Collection
8814 - 19½"x27" (49½x68½ cm)

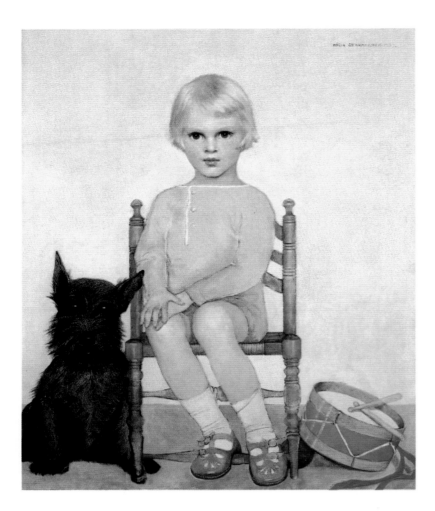

Maria DeKammerer *(Contemporary American)*
BOY WITH DOG, *1933*
Collection of Mr. and Mrs. Henry B. Holt
6240 - 24"x20" (61x51 cm)

Norman Rockwell *(American, 1894-1978)*
PAINTING THE LITTLE HOUSE, *1921*
Collection of Mr. and Mrs. Henry B. Holt
8125 - 27¾"x24" (71x61 cm)

Nat Lewis *(Contemporary American)*
GOOD APPLE YEAR, *1980*
Private Collection
8143 - 16″x23¼″ (40¾x59 cm)

Hubert Shuptrine *(American, 1936-   )*
APPLE PLENTY, *1970*
Private Collection
6013 - 19½″x27½″ (49x69 cm)

Hubert Shuptrine
SEA OF SNOW, *1970*
Private Collection
6014 - 19¾″x27½″ (50x69 cm)

James McNeill Whistler
MOTHER OF THE ARTIST, *1872*
Louvre Museum, Paris
4500 - 11″x14″ (28x35 cm)

William Harnett
MUSIC AND LITERATURE, *1878*
Albright-Knox Art Gallery, Buffalo
4631 - 11″x14″ (28x35 cm)
8631 - 23½″x31½″ (59x79 cm)

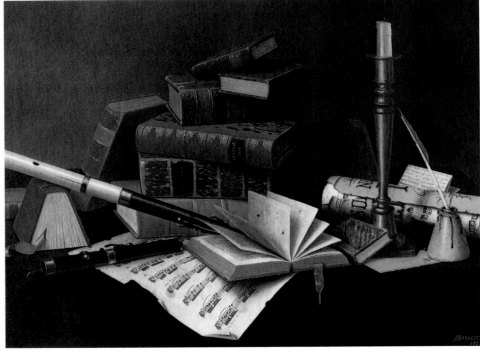

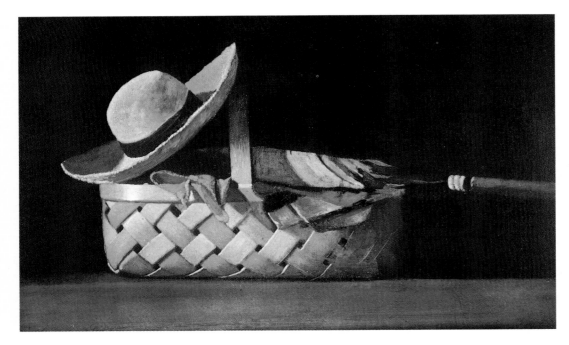

John Frederick Peto
BASKET, UMBRELLA AND HAT
Private Collection
5245 - 10″x16″ (25x40 cm)

Jon S. Legere
NICE AND WARM
Walter von Egidy Collection
7486 - 21¼"x28" (54x71 cm)

Ronald Ekholm *(American, 1942-   )*
TORN SAIL
Private Collection
7970 - 28"x28" (71x71 cm)

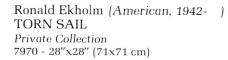

Jon S. Legere *(American, 1944-   )*
WAY INSIDE
Walter von Egidy Collection
7333 - 21¼"x28" (54x71 cm)

Winslow Homer
IN THE MOWING, *1874*
Wichita Art Museum
Roland P. Murdock Collection
5278 - 15¼"x22½" (38x57 cm)

Winslow Homer
WEANING THE CALF, *1875*
The North Carolina Museum of Art, Raleigh
8009 - 19"x30" (48x76 cm)

Winslow Homer
THE MINK POND, *1891*
Fogg Art Museum, Harvard University
5209 - 13¾"x20" (35x51 cm)

Winslow Homer
SKATING AT THE CENTRAL PARK
Winslow Homer Museum, Prout's Neck, Maine
5073 - 12½"x19" (32x48 cm)

Winslow Homer
GLOUCESTER SCHOONERS AND SLOOP
Philadelphia Museum of Art
Gift of Dr. and Mrs. George Woodward
5132 - 13¼"x19¼" (33x48 cm)

Winslow Homer *(American, 1836-1910)*
COUNTRY STORE
Hirshhorn Museum and Sculpture Garden,
Smithsonian Institution
5783 - 11½"x18" (29x46 cm)

Grant Wood
YOUNG CORN, *1931*
Collection of Wilson High School
Cedar Rapids, Iowa
4058 - 12″x16″ (30x40 cm)

Grant Wood
FALL PLOWING, *1931*
Private Collection
4057 - 12″x16″ (30x40 cm)

Grant Wood *(American, 1892-1942)*
AMERICAN GOTHIC, *1930*
The Art Institute of Chicago
3488 - 9½″x7½″ (24x19 cm)
6792 - 20½″x17″ (52x43 cm)

John Rogers Cox *(American, 1915-   )*
GRAY AND GOLD, 1942
Cleveland Museum of Art
7870 - 20″x28″ (51x71 cm)

Thomas Hart Benton
COTTON PICKERS, GEORGIA
Private Collection
5683 - 16″x20″ (40x50 cm)

Edward Lamson Henry (American, 1841-1919)
THE WEDDING
The Fitchburg Art Museum
8863 - 18"x32" (46x81 cm)

Enoch W. Perry, Jr. (American, 1831-1915)
THE PEMIGEWASSET COACH, c. 1899
Shelburne Museum, Shelburne, Vermont
5517 - 11¼"x18" (29x46 cm)
9096 - 22"x35¾" (56x91 cm)

Currier & Ives
THE ROCKY MOUNTAINS
The Harry T. Peters Collection, Museum of the City of New York
4879 - 9½"x14½" (24x36 cm)
7053 - 17½"x25½" (44x65 cm)

Currier & Ives
ACROSS THE CONTINENT
The Harry T. Peters Collection, Museum of the City of New York
7054 - 17½"x27" (44x69 cm)

4883 - WOODCOCK SHOOTING

4879 - THE ROCKY MOUNTAINS

4888 - AMERICAN HUNTING SCENE

NATHANIEL CURRIER AND JAMES MERRITT IVES *(American, Mid-19th Century)*
Plate size approx. 9½"x14½" (24x36 cm)

4889 - CENTRAL PARK, WINTER

4890 - THE ROAD, WINTER

4886 - AMERICAN NATIONAL GAME
OF BASEBALL

4884 - "TROTTING CRACKS" AT THE FORGE

4885 - PEYTONA AND FASHION

NATHANIEL CURRIER AND JAMES MERRITT IVES
Plate size approx. 9½"x14½" (24x36 cm)

4880 - MIDNIGHT RACE ON THE MISSISSIPPI

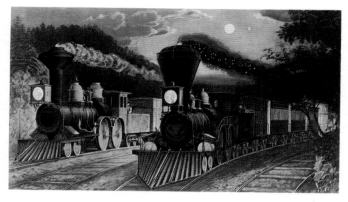

4887 - THE "LIGHTNING EXPRESS" TRAINS

George H. Boughton *(American, b. England, 1833-1905)*
PILGRIMS GOING TO CHURCH, *undated*
The New-York Historical Society
8294 - 17½″x32″ (44x81 cm)

George Caleb Bingham *(American, 1811-1879)*
DANIEL BOONE ESCORTING SETTLERS
THROUGH THE CUMBERLAND GAP, *1851-52*
Washington University Gallery of Art
Steinberg Hall, St. Louis
9300 - 21½″x30″ (54x76 cm)

John Whetton Ehninger
(American, 1827-1889)
OCTOBER, 1867
National Collection of Fine Arts
Smithsonian Institution
8104 - 18″x30″ (46x76 cm)

Alfred C. Howland *(American, 1838-1909)*
FOURTH OF JULY PARADE
Private Collection
9000 - 24"x40" (61x101 cm)

A. M. Willard *(American, 1836-1918)*
THE SPIRIT OF '76, c. 1880
Abbott Hall, Marblehead, Massachusetts
4715 - 14"x10½" (35x26 cm)
7715 - 28"x21" (71x53 cm)

Thomas LeClear *(American, 1818-1882)*
BUFFALO NEWSBOY, 1853
Albright-Knox Art Gallery, Buffalo
6869 - 24"x20" (61x50 cm)

Emanuel Leutze *(American, 1816-1868)*
WASHINGTON CROSSING
THE DELAWARE, *1851*
The Metropolitan Museum of Art, New York
Gift of John S. Kennedy, 1897
4275 - 7½"x13¾" (19x35 cm)
7030 - 18"x30" (46x76 cm)

Unknown Artist
THE WHALER'S FLAG, *c. 1845*
Donaldson, Lufkin & Jenrette, Inc., New York
9053 - 16"x39" (40x99 cm)

John Trumbull *(American, 1756-1843)*
BATTLE OF BUNKER'S HILL
Yale University Art Gallery, New Haven
4276 - 9½"x14" (24x36 cm)
7303 - 22"x30" (56x76 cm)

John Trumbull
DECLARATION OF INDEPENDENCE, *1786-1794*
Yale University Art Gallery, New Haven
4277 - 9"x13¾" (23x35 cm)
7277 - 20"x30" (51x76 cm)

AMERICAN FOLK
and
PRIMITIVE ART

Anna Mary Robertson (Grandma) Moses, page 309

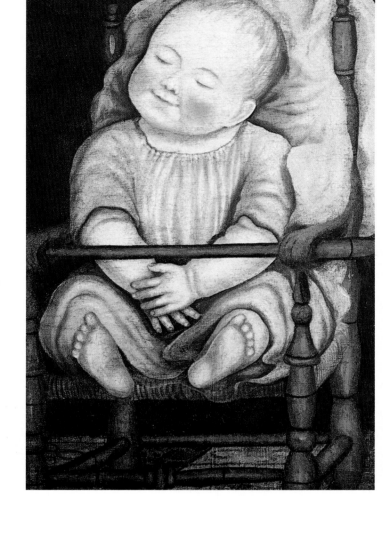

Unknown American Artist
BABY IN RED CHAIR
Abby Aldrich Rockefeller Folk Art Center,
Williamsburg, Virginia
5736 - 21½″x14½″ (56x38 cm)

Attributed to
Erastus Salisbury Field *(American, 19th Century)*
MR. PEARCE *c. 1835*
Abby Aldrich Rockefeller Folk Art Center, Williamsburg, Va.
7237 - 26″x22″ (66x56 cm)

Attributed to
Erastus Salisbury Field *(American, 19th Century)*
MRS. PEARCE *c. 1835*
Abby Aldrich Rockefeller Folk Art Center, Williamsburg, Va.
7238 - 26″x22″ (66x56 cm)

Unknown American Artist
THE QUILTING PARTY
Abby Aldrich Rockefeller Folk Art Center,
Williamsburg, Virginia
6504 - 20"x27¼" (50x69 cm)

Unknown American Artist
FRUIT IN WICKER BASKET, *1870*
Abby Aldrich Rockefeller Folk Art Center,
Williamsburg, Virginia
7283 - 22⅛"x30½" (56x77 cm)

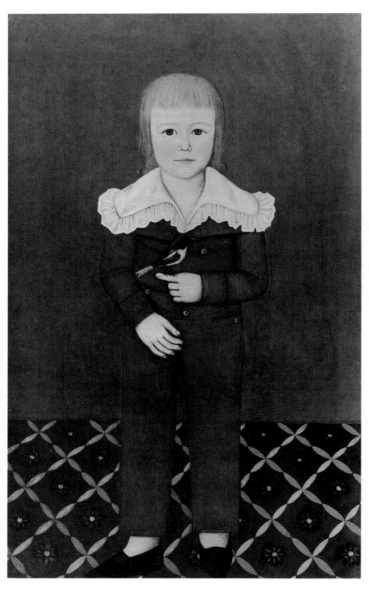

John Brewster, Jr. *(American, 1766-1854)*
BOY WITH FINCH
Abby Aldrich Rockefeller Collection, Williamsburg, Va.
5548 - 19″x11½″ (48x29 cm)
6861 - 28″x17″ (71x43 cm)

Joseph Whiting Stock *(American, 1815-1855)*
MARY JANE SMITH
Abby Aldrich Rockefeller Collection, Williamsburg, Va.
5547 - 19¼″x13¾″ (49x35 cm)
6860 - 28″x20″ (71x51 cm)

Unknown Artist *(American, 19th Century)*
PORTRAIT OF A YOUNG GIRL WITH FLOWERS
M. H. de Young Memorial Museum
6801 - 28"x19" (71x48 cm)

Unknown Artist *(American, 19th Century)*
A YOUNG BOY WITH DOG
M. H. de Young Memorial Museum
6802 - 28"x19" (71x48 cm)

Charles Themmen *(American, 19th Century)*
BARNYARD SCENE, *c. 1860*
Collection of Mr. and Mrs. Henry B. Holt
8124 - 20"x29¾" (50½x75½ cm)

Edward Hicks
THE RESIDENCE OF DAVID TWINING, *1845-1848*
Abby Aldrich Rockefeller Folk Art Center,
Williamsburg, Virginia
6505 - 20¼"x24⅛" (51x61 cm)

Edward Hicks *(American, 1780-1849)*
NOAH'S ARK, *1846*
Philadelphia Museum of Art
Bequest of Lisa Norris Elkins
8699 - 24¼"x28" (61x71 cm)

Edward Hicks
THE PEACEABLE KINGDOM, *1845*
Private Collection
5533 - 13¼"x18" (34x46 cm)
6010 - 17"x23" (43x58 cm)

Unknown American Artist
ALPHABET SAMPLER
Paragon Needlecraft, New York
5261 - 16″x22″ (41x56 cm)

Mary Slatter *(Active 1792)*
SAMPLER, *1792*
Worcester Art Museum
Gift of Mrs. J. Templeman Coolidge
6228 - 17¼″x24″ (44x61 cm)

18th Century Copperplate Textile
THE AVIARY
Private Collection
7987 - 22″x25¼″ (56x64 cm)

Unknown American Artist *(mid-Nineteenth Century)*
LEAPING DEER
Abby Aldrich Rockefeller Folk Art Center,
Williamsburg, Virginia
6503 - 20″x26⅞″ (51x68 cm)

Edward Hicks
THE FALLS OF NIAGARA, 1825
The Metropolitan Museum of Art, New York
Gift of William and Bernice Chrysler Garbisch, 1962
8654 - 26¾"x32" (68x81 cm)
18"x23" (46x60 cm) without border

Edward Hicks
THE PEACEABLE KINGDOM OF THE
BRANCH, *1830-40*
Abby Aldrich Rockefeller Folk Art Center,
Williamsburg, Virginia
6096 - 22½"x26½" (57x67 cm)
16"x20¼" (41x51½ cm) without border

Horace Pippin (*American, 1888-1946*)
HOLY MOUNTAIN III, *1945*
Joseph H. Hirshhorn Collection
7302 - 23½"x28" (60x71 cm)

Hannibal Lee (*Contemporary American*)
ORPHEUS AND THE ANIMALS
Private Collection
6464 - 22"x28" (56x71 cm)

Anna Mary Robertson (Grandma) Moses *(American, 1860-1961)*
THE OLD CHECKERED HOUSE IN WINTER, *1950*
Estate of Otto Kallir
6889 - 20¼″x24½″ (51½x62 cm)

Anna Mary Robertson (Grandma) Moses *(American, 1860-1961)*
HOOSICK RIVER, SUMMER, *1952*
Private Collection, Courtesy Galerie St. Etienne
6059 - 18½″x24½″ (47x62¼ cm)

Anna Mary Robertson (Grandma) Moses *(American, 1860-1961)*
A BEAUTIFUL WORLD, *1948*
Private Collection
6469 - 18"x24" (45¾x61 cm)

Anna Mary Robertson (Grandma) Moses *(American, 1860-1961)*
SUGARING OFF, *1955*
Private Collection
6468 - 18"x24" (45¾x61 cm)

Joseph Pickett *(American, 1848-1918)*
MANCHESTER VALLEY, *1914-18*
The Museum of Modern Art, New York
7251 - 22¼"x29¾" (56x75 cm)

Peter Blume *(American, 1906-   )*
THE BOAT, *1929*
The Museum of Modern Art, New York
5033 - 16½"x20" (42x51 cm)

Barbara Bustetter Falk *(American, 1928-   )*
MY GARDEN, *1976*
Private Collection
6893 - 26"x22½" (66x57 cm)

Barbara Bustetter Falk
HEIDI, *1970*
Private Collection
6892 - 20"x25" (51x63 cm)

Henri Rousseau
THE WATERFALL, *1910*
The Art Institute of Chicago
8825 - 24"x31" (61x79 cm)

Henri Rousseau *(French, 1844-1910)*
VIRGIN FOREST AT SUNSET, *1907*
Kunstmuseum, Basel
7256 - 19½"x27½" (49x70 cm)

Henri Rousseau
THE EQUATORIAL JUNGLE, *1909*
National Gallery of Art, Washington, D.C.
Chester Dale Collection
7254 - 26″x23½″ (65x60 cm)

Henri Rousseau
THE CART OF PERE JUNIET, *1908*
Musée de l'Orangerie, Paris
8286 - 23½″x31¾″ (60x80 cm)

Henri Rousseau
TIGER HUNT, *1895*
Columbus Gallery of Fine Arts
Columbus, Ohio
5724 - 16½″x20″ (42x50 cm)

HUNTING
SPORTS and GAMES

Page 323

James Seymour *(British, 18th Century)*
Engraved by Smith of London
THE POINTERS AND THE HARE
Collection of The Colonial Williamsburg Foundation
Williamsburg, VA
5983 - 16"x21¾" (40½x55¼ cm)

James Seymour *(British, 18th Century)*
Engraved by Smith of London
THE SETTING DOGS AND PARTRIDGES
Collection of The Colonial Williamsburg Foundation
Williamsburg, VA
5984 - 16"x21¾" (40½x55¼ cm)

George Stubbs *(British, 18th Century)*
SWEET WILLIAM
Collection of The Colonial Williamsburg Foundation
Williamsburg, VA
6554 - 15″x19″ (38x48¼ cm)

James Seymour *(British, 18th Century)*
FOX HUNTING: IN FULL CRY
Collection of the Colonial Williamsburg Foundation
8175 - 20″x25½″ (50¾x64¾ cm)

James Seymour *(British, 18th Century)*
Engraved by Smith of London
THE CHASE
Collection of The Colonial Williamsburg Foundation
Williamsburg, VA
5985 - 16"x21¾" (40½x55¼ cm)

James Seymour *(British, 18th Century)*
Engraved by Smith of London
MAKING A CAST AT A FAULT
Collection of The Colonial Williamsburg Foundation
Williamsburg, VA
5987 - 16"x21¾" (40½x55¼ cm)

GOING TO COVER.

L'ENTREE DU BOIS.

James Seymour *(British, 18th Century)*
Engraved by Smith of London
GOING TO COVER
Collection of The Colonial Williamsburg Foundation
Williamsburg, VA
5986 - 16"x21¾" (40½x55¼ cm)

THE DEATH OF THE FOX.

LA MORT DU RENARD

James Seymour *(British, 18th Century)*
Engraved by Smith of London
THE DEATH OF THE FOX
Collection of The Colonial Williamsburg Foundation
Williamsburg, VA
5988 - 16"x21¾" (40½x55¼ cm)

HUNTING SPORTS & GAMES   319

THE MEET
3741 - 6½"x11" (16x28 cm)
6741 - 13"x20½" (33x52 cm)

J.F. Herring, Sr. *(British, 1795-1865)*
HUNTING SCENES
Series: 3741-4; 6741-4

FULL CRY
3743 - 6½"x11" (16x28 cm)
6743 - 13"x20½" (33x52 cm)

BREAKING COVER
3742 - 6½″x11″ (16x28 cm)
6742 - 13″x20½″ (33x52 cm)

END OF HUNT
3744 - 6½″x11″ (16x28 cm)
6744 - 13″x20½″ (33x52 cm)

George Morland *(British, 1763-1804)*
THE END OF THE HUNT, *c. 1794*
National Gallery of Art, Washington, D.C.
Widener Collection
8745 - 23½″x31″ (59x78 cm)

Nicolas Lancret *(French, 1690-1743)*
THE PICNIC AFTER THE HUNT, *c. 1740*
National Gallery of Art, Washington, D.C.
Samuel H. Kress Collection
7264 - 23½″x29″ (59x74 cm)

Wordsworth Thompson *(American, 1840-1896)*
THE DEPARTING GUESTS, *1889*
The New-York Historical Society
9538 - 21½"x36" (55x91 cm)

Unknown English Artist *(Early 19th Century)*
CRICKET MATCH AT KENFIELD HALL
The Marlyebone Cricket Club, London
7385 - 20"x30½" (51x77½ cm)

Carolyn Wright *(Contemporary American)*
MISTY MORNING MALLARDS, *1984*
Collection of Linda Lewis and George Stein
6992 - 16"x24" (40½x61 cm)

Bruce Lattig
PHEASANT JUMPING, *1969*
Private Collection
6518 - 29"x21" (73x53 cm)

Bruce Lattig
PHEASANT HOLDING, *1969*
Private Collection
6519 - 20½"x29" (52x73 cm)

James M. Sessions
TROUT STREAM
Private Collection
7564 - 20″x26″ (51x66 cm)

James M. Sessions *(American, 1882-1962)*
GROUSE SHOOTING
Private Collection
7562 - 20″x26″ (51x66 cm)

Thomas Eakins
PUSHING FOR RAIL, *1874*
The Metropolitan Museum of Art, New York
6006 - 14″x21½″ (35x54 cm)

Thomas Eakins
WILL SCHUSTER AND BLACKMAN GOING SHOOTING, *1876*
Yale University Art Gallery, New Haven
3171 - 7″x9½″ (17x24 cm)

Thomas Eakins *(American, 1844-1916)*
BASEBALL PLAYERS PRACTICING, *1875*
Museum of Art
Rhode Island School of Design
3800 - 10¼″x11¾″ (26x30 cm)

Paul Sample *(American, 1896-1974)*
BOYS' SKI OUTING, *1963*
Kimball Union Academy, Meriden, New Hampshire
9285 - 25¾"x35¾" (65x91 cm)

Dwight Shepler *(American, 1905-   )*
ON THE GLACIER
5432 - 14"x20" (35x51 cm)

Churchill Ettinger *(American, 1903-   )*
THE CHOICE, *1970*
Private Collection
7308 - 20½"x28½" (52x72 cm)

FLOWERS
and
FRUIT

Janet Walsh,   page 336

Tjelda Michas *(Contemporary American)*
SPRING BULBS
Private Collection
7629 - 22″x20¼″ (56x51½ cm)

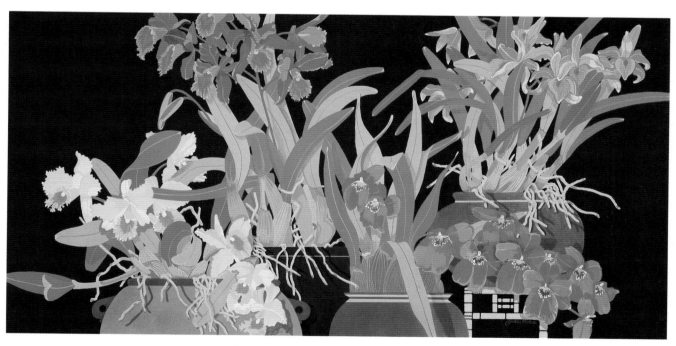

Tjelda Michas *(Contemporary American)*
BRAZILIAN ORCHID
Private Collection
8162 - 16¼″x32″ (41x81 cm)

Barbara Nechis *(Contemporary American)*
POPPIES, *1981*
Collection of the Artist
7501 - 22″x30″ (56x76 cm)

Barbara Nechis *(Contemporary American)*
FESTIVAL, *1981*
Private Collection
6858 - 22¼″x15″ (56½x38 cm)

Barbara Nechis *(Contemporary American)*
HOLIDAY, *1981*
Private Collection
6859 - 22¼″x15″ (56½x38 cm)

Leonard Brooks *(Contemporary Canadian)*
AMARYLLIS AND CAT
Collection of the Artist
8126 - 28"x24¾" (71x63 cm)

Leonard Brooks *(Contemporary Canadian)*
IRIS AND POND
Collection of the Artist
8127 - 30"x19" (76x48 cm)

Virginia Greenleaf *(Contemporary American)*
CHRYSANTHEMUMS AND DAISIES, *1982*
The Main Street Gallery Nantucket Inc.
8133 - 30"x30" (76x76 cm)

M.H. Hurlimann Armstrong *(Contemporary American)*
MY FRIEND'S GARDEN, *1979*
Collection of the Artist
6816 - 18"x24" (46x61 cm)

Patti Vaughn *(Contemporary American)*
FLORAL SPRAY, *1985*
Collection of the Artist
6993 - 22"x15¼" (56x38¾ cm)

Patti Vaughn *(Contemporary American)*
SUMMER BOUQUET, *1985*
Collection of the Artist
6994 - 22"x15¼" (56x38¾ cm)

Vivian Angel
WILD IRISES, *1985*
Private Collection
9987 - 24"x32" (61x81 cm)

Lorraine E'drie *(Contemporary American)*
SUMMER BLOSSOMS/SUMMER PORCH, *1985*
Private Collection
8812 - diptych (two panels)
Each panel 28½″x21½″ (72½x54½ cm)

Janet B. Walsh *(Contemporary American)*
EMMA'S BOWL, *1984*
Private Collection
7084 - 20″x27″ (50¾x68½ cm)

Arthur Cady *(American, 1920-   )*
THE COUNTRY BOUQUET
Private Collection
5525 - 18″x14½″ (46x37 cm)
7797 - 28″x22″ (71x56 cm)

Piero Aversa *(Contemporary Italian)*
FLOWERS OF MYKONOS
Private Collection
8390 - 31″x24″ (79x61 cm)

Ann Levere *(Contemporary American)*
FLOWER DECOR, *1982*
Private Collection
7230 - 24″x18″ (61x45¾ cm)

Ann Levere *(Contemporary American)*
IRIS, MIXED FLORAL, *1983*
Private Collection
7231 - 24″x18″ (61x45¾ cm)

Bill Stark *(Contemporary American)*
LAS FLORES MEJICANAS, *1967*
Private Collection
7229 - 23¾″x27½″ (60½x70 cm)

M.H. Hurlimann Armstrong *(Contemporary American)*
ESTHER'S FLOWERS
Collection of the Artist
6268 - 20¼″x26″ (51½x66 cm)

Ken Davies *(Contemporary American)*
END OF SEASON, *1977*
Collection of Mrs. Charles Hofrichter
5346 - 16½"x11¼" (42x28½ cm)

Paul Cézanne
VASE OF TULIPS, *c. 1890-94*
The Art Institute of Chicago
613 - 22¼"x16" (56x40 cm)

Paul Cézanne
THE BLUE VASE, *1883-87*
Louvre Museum, Paris
5926 - 20"x15½" (50x40 cm)

Piet Mondrian
BLUE ROSE, *c. 1922*
Private Collection
4989 - 10¾"x7¾" (27x19 cm)

Piet Mondrian
BLUE CHRYSANTHEMUM, *c. 1922*
Private Collection
4988 - 11"x9½" (27x24 cm)

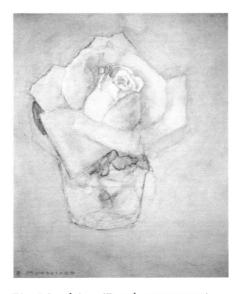

Piet Mondrian *(Dutch, 1872-1944)*
ROSE IN A TUMBLER, *c. 1922*
Private Collection
4991 - 9½"x7½" (23x19 cm)

Piet Mondrian
LARGE CHRYSANTHEMUM, *c. 1908*
Private Collection
4990 - 16"x9¾" (40x24 cm)

Piet Mondrian
RHODODENDRON, *c. 1905*
Santa Barbara Museum of Art, Calif.
7017 - 18"x28½" (46x72 cm)

Raoul Dufy
GLADIOLI, 1942
Private Collection
6664 - 24″x18½″ (61x47 cm)

Charles Demuth
FLOWER STUDY NUMBER ONE, *1923*
The Art Institute of Chicago
5816 - 18″x12″ (46x30 cm)

Charles Demuth *(American, 1883-1935)*
FLOWER STUDY NUMBER FOUR, *1925*
The Art Institute of Chicago
5817 - 18″x12″ (46x30 cm)

Kamil Kubik *(b. Czechoslovakia, 1930-   )*
SUMMER ABUNDANCE
Private Collection
7496 - 24″x26″ (61x66 cm)

Odilon Redon *(French, 1840-1916)*
WILDFLOWERS, *c. 1905*
National Gallery of Art, Washington, D.C.
5530 - 18″x13″ (46x33 cm)
6394 - 24″x18″ (61x46 cm)

Odilon Redon
BOUQUET OF FLOWERS IN A GREEN VASE, *c. 1906*
Wadsworth Atheneum, Hartford, Conn.
7097 - 28″x20¼″ (71x51 cm)

Bernard Cathelin
LE VASE BLANC, 1962
Private Collection
4615 - 14″x9″ (35x22 cm)
7495 - 28″x21¼″ (71x54 cm)

Bernard Cathelin
SPRING, 1963
Private Collection
7493 - 28″x18″ (71x46 cm)

Bernard Cathelin
SUMMER, 1963
Private Collection
7492 - 28″x18″ (71x46 cm)

Mark Adams *(Contemporary American)*
RANUNCULAS
Collection of Elizabeth Banning, A.I.D.
7391 - 28"x25" (71x63 cm)

Four Watercolors by Emil Nolde
(German, 1867-1956)
Norton Simon Foundation
Series 3767-3770

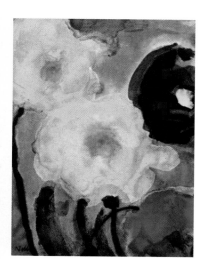

RED, YELLOW AND BLUE FLOWERS
3769 - 9¼"x6¾" (23x17 cm)

RED DAHLIAS
3767 - 9"x11" (23x28 cm)

YELLOW SUNFLOWERS AND RED POPPIES
3770 - 10¾"x12¾" (27x32 cm)

RED POPPIES AND LARKSPUR
3768 - 9"x10¼" (23x26 cm)

FLOWERS & FRUIT   **343**

Steven R. Miller *(Contemporary American)*
ZINNIAS IN YELLOW VASE, *1981*
Collection of Jeffrey Kurzweil
8141 - 26″x19″ (66x48¼ cm)

Marsden Hartley *(American, 1877-1943)*
STILL LIFE NO. 9
University of Minnesota Gallery, Minneapolis
6665 - 25″x20¾″ (63x53 cm)

Carol Auer
APRIL FLOWERS, *1971*
Private Collection
8953 - 28″x23¼″ (71x59 cm)

Frans Oerder (German, 1876-1942)
MAGNOLIAS
8393 - 25½"x32" (65x81 cm)

Unknown American Artist
FLOWERS AND FRUIT, c. 1830
National Gallery of Art, Washington, D.C.
7733 - 26"x19½" (66x49 cm)

Sidney Loeb (American, 1904-1972)
MOONFLOWERS, 1960
Collection of Mrs. Sidney Loeb
7804 - 31"x24" (78x61 cm)

T. Jefferys
PLATE NO. 23
Special Collections of the Colonial Williamsburg Foundation Library
8173 - 20″x12½″ (50¾x31¾ cm)

T. Jefferys *(British, 18th Century)*
PLATE NO. 24
Special Collections of the Colonial Williamsburg Foundation Library
8174 - 20″x12½″ (50¾x31¾ cm)

James Peale *(American, 1749-1831)*
STILL LIFE WITH FRUIT
M.H. de Young Memorial Museum, San Francisco, Calif.
6524 - 18¼"x25¼" (46x64 cm)

James Peale
FRUIT, *c. 1820*
The Corcoran Gallery of Art, Washington, D.C.
7826 - 17"x27" (43x68 cm)

Francesco Guardi *(Italian, 1712-1793)*
FLOWERS, *undated*
Rijksmuseum, Amsterdam
7481 - 21¼"x30¾" (54x78 cm)

Ryszard Ploskonka *(Contemporary Polish)*
FLORAL STILL LIFE, *1976*
Private Collection
7093 - 28″x22″ (71x56 cm)

Jean-Baptiste Monnoyer
A FLOWER PIECE
Chrysler Museum at Norfolk
8109 - 31″x24¼″ (79x62 cm)

Jean-Baptiste Monnoyer *(French, 1634-1699)*
FLOWER PIECE, POPPIES AND MARIGOLDS
Norton Simon, Inc. Museum of Art, Pasadena
7872 - 24″x30″ (61x76 cm)

Juan de Arellano *(Spanish, 1614-1676)*
HYDRANGEAS WITH TULIPS, *1664*
Rockoxhuis Museum, Antwerp
9641 - 36″x15¾″ (91x40 cm)

Juan de Arellano
ROSES WITH BLUE IRIS, *1664*
Rockoxhuis Museum, Antwerp
9642 - 36″x15¾″ (91x40 cm)

Anton Doring
GARDEN GLORY
5764 - 20″x15½″ (50x39 cm)

Michael Janch
GARDEN FLOWERS
4767 - 14″x11″ (35x28 cm)
5763 - 20″x15½″ (50x39 cm)

Martin Fromhold
SUMMER BOUQUET, 1802
6706 - 22″x16″ (56x41 cm)

Josef Bittner
JUNE FLOWERS
6708 - 22″x16″ (56x41 cm)

J.M. van Nikkelen *(Dutch, born c. 1690)*
JUNE BLOSSOMS
Akademie der Bildenden Künste, Vienna
5767 - 20"x16" (51x40 cm)

Jan van Huysum
GARDEN GAIETY
Akademie der Bildenden Künste, Vienna
5766 - 20"x16" (51x40 cm)

Rachel Ruysch *(Dutch, 1664-1750)*
IN FULL BLOOM
Akademie der Bildenden Künste, Vienna
5768 - 20"x16" (51x40 cm)

Malcolm Thompson
MISTY MORNING
Private Collection
5505 - 13¼″x18″ (34x46 cm)
7933 - 25″x34″ (63x86 cm)

Lydia Kemeny
GERANIUMS
Private Collection
5520 - 18″x11″ (46x28 cm)
8292 - 32″x20″ (81x50 cm)

Lydia Kemeny
BLUE SHUTTERS, *1969*
Private Collection
4098 - 18″x12″ (45x30 cm)

Russ Elliott *(Contemporary American)*
GARDEN CHAIR
Collection of the Artist
5500 - 13½"x18" (34x46 cm)
9064 - 24"x32" (61x81 cm)

Carol Auer *(Contemporary American)*
SUMMER FRAGRANCE, *1970*
Private Collection
7814 - 22"x28" (55x71 cm)

Lydia Kemeny
IN A COURTYARD
5519 - 18"x13¼" (46x29 cm)

FLOWERS & FRUIT 353

Mimi Conkling
FLORAL FANTASY
Private Collection
7657 - 22"x30" (56x76 cm)

Mimi Conkling
A WOODLAND GLEN
Private Collection
6620 - 20"x24" (51x61 cm)

Mimi Conkling
A MEADOW CORNER
Private Collection
6619 - 20"x24" (51x61 cm)

Mimi Conkling *(Contemporary American)*
PENSIVE
Private Collection
6618 - 24″x20″ (61x51 cm)

Mimi Conkling
CURIOSITY
Private Collection
6617 - 24″x20″ (61x51 cm)

Cynthia Augeri
SPRING FLORAL WITH SONG SPARROW
Private Collection
6915 - 26″x20″ (66x51 cm)

Cynthia Augeri
AUTUMN FLORAL WITH GOLDEN CROWN KINGLET
Private Collection
6914 - 26″x20″ (66x51 cm)

Ida Pellei
PRIMAVERA
Private Collection
7930 - 24″x30″ (61x76 cm)

Ida Pellei
SUMMER AFTERNOON
Private Collection
9065 - 24″x36″ (61x91 cm)

Ida Pellei
YELLOW TULIPS
Private Collection
7505 - 31¾"x24" (81x61 cm)

Ida Pellei
FERNS WITH MIXED BASKET
Private Collection
7504 - 31¾"x24" (81x61 cm)

Ida Pellei *(Contemporary American)*
JOYS OF SUMMER
Private Collection
7956 - 28"x28" (71x71 cm)

Ida Pellei
FIELD FLOWERS AND FERN
Private Collection
5551 - 16"x12" (41x30 cm)

Ida Pellei
DAISIES AND STRAWBERRIES, *1976*
Private Collection
7915 - 24"x24" (61x61 cm)

Ida Pellei
YELLOW DAISIES AND MARGUERITES
Private Collection
5553 - 12"x16" (30x41 cm)

Ida Pellei
ORANGE ZINNIAS AND GREENERY
Private Collection
5552 - 12"x16" (30x41 cm)

Harold McIntosh
BY A WOODLAND STREAM, *1979*
Collection of Beverly A. McIntosh
7570 - 28⅜″x22″ (72x55 cm)

Harold McIntosh
MOVING DAY FOR THE MARSH MARIGOLDS
Private Collection
6450 - 21¼″x26¼″ (54x67 cm)

Ida Pellei
SUNFLOWERS, *1976*
Private Collection
8826 - 24″x32″ (61x81 cm)

STILL LIFES

Susan Stokes,　page 362

Elsie Manville *(Contemporary American)*
MCINTOSH APPLES IN A WHITE BOWL, *1981*
Collection of Moe Shapiro
5347 - 14"x19" (35½x48¼ cm)

Susan Murray Stokes *(Contemporary British)*
CHARDIN INSPIRATION
Collection of Lexington Depositors Trust Company
6624 - 19½"x27" (49½x68½ cm)

Susan Murray Stokes *(Contemporary British)*
THE MING GOBLET, *1984*
Collection of Jose Fonseca
6406 - 23½"x20" (59½x50¾ cm)

Olive Reich *(Contemporary American)*
IT'S SUMMER, *1984*
Private Collection
8150 - 19"x26" (48¼x66 cm)

Diana Barnes *(Contemporary American)*
SAILBOATS THROUGH THE WINDOWS
Collection of Bettina Mead & Assoc.
8161 - 20"x27" (50¾x68½ cm)

Carl Broemel
GREEN QUINCES
Private Collection
5250 - 18¾"x24" (48x61 cm)

Carlo Carrà *(Italian, 1881-1966)*
STILL LIFE, *1957*
Dr. Antonio Mazzotta Collection, Milan
6659 - 23½"x19¾" (60x50 cm)

Carl Broemel *(American, 1891-   )*
GERANIUM AND GREEN QUINCES
Private Collection
5444 - 15¾"x22" (40x56 cm)

James Ensor
EFFECT OF LIGHT
Tate Gallery, London
6765 - 19"x22¾" (50x69 cm)

Thesis Newer
STILL LIFE WITH BASKET, *1976*
Private Collection
7929 - 30"x24" (76x61 cm)

Anders Gisson (*Contemporary American*)
ALONG THE SEINE
Private Collection
7997 - 24"x30" (61x76 cm)

Anne La Bouriau *(Contemporary French)*
AUTUMN
Private Collection
8134 - 30"x24¼" (76x61½ cm)

Henri Fantin-Latour *(French, 1836-1904)*
BOUQUET DE JULIENNE ET FRUITS
The Fine Arts Museums of San Francisco
6704 - 22"x21" (56x53½ cm)

Julia Lopez *(Contemporary Mexican)*
STILL LIFE WITH DOVE, *1967*
Private Collection
6239 - 20"x24" (51x61 cm)

Charles Dufresne *(French, 1876-1938)*
STILL LIFE, *1927-28*
National Gallery of Art, Washington, D.C.
Chester Dale Collection
7222 - 24¼″x30″ (62x76 cm)

Alexandru Ciucurencu *(Rumanian, 1903-   )*
CYCLAMEN, *1944*
Art Museum of the Rumanian People's Republic, Bucharest
6311 - 19″x23½″ (48x59 cm)

Attributed to:
Juan van der Hamen *(Spanish, 1596-1631)*
STILL LIFE, *undated*
Thyssen-Bornemisza Collection, Lugano
8280 - 23¾"x31¾" (60x81 cm)

Attributed to: Juan van der Hamen
STILL LIFE: FLOWERS AND FRUIT (detail)
The Art Institute of Chicago
4189 - 10¼"x13¼" (26x35 cm)

Willem Kalf (Dutch, 1622-1693)
STILL LIFE, 1665
National Gallery of Art, Washington, D.C.
7485 - 26"x21½" (66x55 cm)

Henri-Horace Roland de la Porte (French, 1724-1793)
STILL LIFE, c. 1765
Norton Simon, Inc. Museum of Art
5526 - 14½"x17½" (37x45 cm)
6357 - 20"x24½" (51x62 cm)

Louise Moillon *(French, 1610-1696)*
STILL LIFE WITH CHERRIES,
STRAWBERRIES AND GOOSEBERRIES
The Norton Simon Foundation
5554 - 14″x21¼″ (36x54 cm)

Jean-Baptiste Siméon Chardin *(French, 1699-1779)*
A BOWL OF PLUMS, *undated*
The Phillips Collection, Washington, D.C.
640 - 16″x20½″ (40x52 cm)

Jean-Baptiste Siméon Chardin *(French, 1699-1779)*
THE ATTRIBUTES OF THE ARTS, *1766*
The Minneapolis Institute of Arts
8295 - 24¾″x32″ (63x81 cm)

Salvador Dalí
BASKET OF BREAD, *1926*
Collection of Mr. and Mrs. A. Reynolds Morse
4164 - 12½″x12½″ (32x32 cm)

William Harnett
THE OLD REFRAIN, *1886*
Private Collection
6630 - 22½″x15½″ (57x39 cm)

John Frederick Peto
LETTER RACK
Private Collection
6981 - 25″x21″ (63x53 cm)

Georges Braque
VIOLIN AND PIPE
(with the word POLKA), *1920-21*
Philadelphia Museum of Art
The Louise and Walter Arensberg Collection
9286 - 17"x36" (43x91 cm)

Gino Severini
STILL LIFE WITH MANDOLIN AND FRUIT, *1920-25*
Stedelijk Museum, Amsterdam
On loan from the State Collection
6694 - 17"x21" (43x53 cm)

Juan Gris *(Spanish, 1887-1927)*
STILL LIFE WITH OPEN BOOK, *1925*
Private Collection
508 - 16"x20" (40x50 cm)

Miguel Ibarz Roca *(Spanish, 1920-   )*
BLUE VASE
Private Collection
7317 - 28″x22″ (71x56 cm)

Rose Gaynor Barrett *(American, 1884-1954)*
SEA TREASURE, *c. 1940*
6090 - 19½″x26″ (50x66 cm)

Bernard Buffet *(French, 1928-   )*
THE BREAKFAST, *1955*
Private Collection
7023 - 25½″x19½″ (65x49 cm)

Lydia Kemeny
THE RED CHAIR
Collection Neville S. Conrad
4099 - 18″x12″ (45x30 cm)
8289 - 32″x19¾″ (81x50 cm)

Bernard Buffet
STILL LIFE: THE LOBSTER, *1958*
Private Collection
7038 - 20½″x27½″ (52x70 cm)

ORIENTAL

Sakai Hoitsu,   page 380

Cho Tai Eok *(Korean, 1675-1728)*
TWO HARES IN MOONLIGHT
Philadelphia Museum of Art
8255 - 34"x11½" (86x29 cm)

Sakai Hoitsu
IRIS AND MANDARIN DUCKS
Dallas Museum of Fine Arts
8098 - 34"x14" (84x36 cm)

Sakai Hoitsu
(Japanese, 1761-1828) Edo Period
AUTUMN FLOWERS AND MOON
Freer Gallery of Art, Washington, D.C.
8025 - 32¾"x11½" (83x29 cm)

ORIENTAL   379

Sakai Hoitsu *(Japanese-Tokugawa Period, 1761-1828)*
CRANES
Worcester Art Museum
5515 - 14½"x14½" (37x37 cm)
9069 - 27¼"x27¼" (69x69 cm)

Ogata Korin *(Japanese, 1658-1716)*
CRANES
Freer Gallery of Art, Washington, D.C.
9059 - 17¼"x39" (44x99 cm)

Unknown Japanese Artist *(Early 17th Century)*
PORTUGUESE SHIP ENTERING A JAPANESE HARBOR
(1st of pair of six-fold Japanese screens), Rijksmuseum, Amsterdam
9634 - 19"x42" (48x106 cm)

Fukaye Roshu *(Japanese, 1699-1757)*
THE PASS THROUGH
THE MOUNTAINS (MOUNT UTSU)
The Cleveland Museum of Art
John L. Severance Fund
9674 - 20¼"x40¼" (51x103 cm)

Unknown Japanese Artist *(Early 17th Century)*
PORTUGUESE VISITORS ARRIVING IN JAPAN
(2nd of pair of six-fold Japanese screens), Rijksmuseum, Amsterdam
9635 - 19"x42" (48x106 cm)

Unknown Japanese Artist *(18th Century)*
CHRYSANTHEMUMS
Collection of Ciancimino Limited, London
9552 - 16¾"x37¾" (43x95½ cm)

Unknown Japanese Artist *(Late 16th-Early 17th Century)*
CRANES AND FLOWERS
Collection of Ciancimino Limited, London
9553 - 16¾"x37¾" (43x95½ cm)

Unknown Japanese Artist *(18th Century)*
A FLOWER CART
Milne Henderson Collection, London
9981 - 17"x33¾" (43x86 cm)

Li Sheng *(Chinese, 1271-1368)*
SAYING FAREWELL BY THE LAKE DIANSHAN, *1346*
Shanghai Museum
7900 - 9″x29¾″ (23x75½ cm)

Unknown Japanese Artist *(19th Century)*
CRANES AND BLOSSOMING TREES
Ariane Faye, Paris
9646 - 16″x38″ (41x96½ cm)

Unknown Japanese Artist *(19th Century)*
CRANES ALONG A RIVER
Ariane Faye, Paris
9645 - 16″x38″ (41x96½ cm)

Sakai Hoitsu
PAULOWNIAS AND CHRYSANTHEMUMS
The Cleveland Museum of Art
5503 - 14½″x14½″ (37x37 cm)
8101 - 28″x28½″ (71x72 cm)

Unknown Japanese Artist *(Late 18th Century)*
FANS
Collection of Spink and Son Ltd., London
7036 - 30″x22″ (76x56 cm)

So Shiseki
PARAKEETS AND HYDRANGEA
Private Collection
5025 - 13¾″x22¾″ (35x58 cm)

Shen Ch'uan
FLOWERS AND BIRDS, c. 1758
Nelson Gallery-Atkins Museum
Kansas City, Missouri
8686 - 34"x14" (86x36 cm)

Watanabe Shiko
(Japanese, 1683-1755)
FLOWERS
Freer Gallery of Art,
Washington, D.C.
5521 - 18"x9½"
(46x24 cm)
8367 - 33"x17¾"
(84x45 cm)

Lang Shih-Ning *(Giusseppe Castiglione)*
(Born: Milan, Italy, 1688; Died: Peking, China, 1766)
EIGHT IMPERIAL HORSES
Alice Boney Collection, New York
9305 - 18"x34" (45x86 cm)

Tosa Mitsuoki, *(Japanese, 1617-1691)*
QUAILS AND FLOWERS
Museum of Asiatic Art
Rijksmuseum, Amsterdam
5096 - 16″x16″ (40x40 cm)

Unknown Chinese Artist
(Ming Dynasty, 1368-1644)
BASKET FILLED WITH FLOWERS
Museum of Asiatic Art
Rijksmuseum, Amsterdam
5095 - 16″x16″ (40x40 cm)

Yun Shou-p'ing *(Chinese, 1633-1690)*
CAMELIAS, PLUM BLOSSOMS,
PEONIES AND MAGNOLIA
(Detail, "One Hundred Flowers")
Collection of Mr. John M. Crawford, Jr., New York
8111 - 15½"x34" (39x86 cm)

Yun Shou-p'ing
ROSES AND IRIS
Collection of Mr. John M. Crawford, Jr., New York
5663 - 16"x16" (40x40 cm)

Yun Shou-p'ing
CHERRY BLOSSOMS AND WILD ROSES
Collection of Mr. John M. Crawford, Jr., New York
5664 - 16"x16" (40x40 cm)

T'ang Yin *(Chinese, 1470-1523)*
DRUNKEN FISHERMAN BY A REED BANK
(From a Hanging Scroll)
Collection of Mr. John M. Crawford, Jr., New York
7198 - 28½"x14½" (71x37 cm)

Maruyama Okyo *(Japanese, 1733-1795)*
GEESE IN FLIGHT
Courtesy of the Alice Boney Gallery, New York
7516 - 28"x28¼" (71x71 cm)

T'ang Ti *(Chinese, 1296-c. 1364)*
PAVILION OF PRINCE T'ENG
Collection of Mr. John M. Crawford, Jr., New York
7088 - 9⅞"x30" (25x76 cm)

Ch'ien Hsuan *(Chinese-Yuan Dynasty, 1236-1368)*
EARLY AUTUMN
Detroit Institute of Arts
8850 - 8"x36" (20x91 cm)

Unknown Chinese Artist *(Yuan Dynasty, 1260-1368)*
TRIBUTE HORSES
Indianapolis Museum of Art
Gift of J.W. Alsdorf
5358 - 14"x16½" (35x41 cm)

Ikeda Koson *(Japanese, 1802-1867)* Edo Period
CYPRESS TREES
Private Collection
8854 - 31½"x33" (80x84 cm)

Attributed to Han-Kan *(Chinese, VIII Century)*
TARTARS BRINGING A TRIBUTE OF HORSES
Freer Gallery of Art, Washington, D.C.
9281 - 12¼"x40" (31x101 cm)

Unknown Chinese Artist *(14th Century)*
THREE HORSES
(Detail of Handscroll)
Collection of Mr. John M. Crawford, Jr., New York
8112 - 16"x32" (40x81 cm)

Unknown Chinese Artist *(Early 19th Century)*
MANDARIN DUCKS IN LANDSCAPE
Collection of Toynbee-Clarke Interiors, London
7557 - 18¾"x30" (47½x76 cm)

Unknown Chinese Artist
MANDARIN DUCKS BY A STREAM
Private Collection
9073 - 33¾"x17" (86x43 cm)

Tosa Mitsuoki *(Japanese, 1617-1691)*
CHRYSANTHEMUM AND QUAIL
Virginia Museum of Fine Arts, Richmond
8022 - 34"x14¾" (86x38 cm)

Unknown Chinese Artist
TWO KITTENS BY A POOL
Private Collection
8518 - 33¾"x17" (86x43 cm)

So Ryu
THE FLOWER CART
Private Collection
5514 - 9"x18" (23x46 cm)
8684 - 17½"x34" (44x86 cm)

Barbara Nechis *(Contemporary American)*
FLOWER FANTASY
Private Collection
6376 - 15″x22″ (38x56 cm)

Barbara Nechis
SUMMER SILHOUETTE
Private Collection
6377 - 15″x22″ (38x56 cm)

Hui Chi Mau
GRAPES AND SONGBIRD
Private Collection
5607 - 20¾"x18" (53x46 cm)

Hui Chi Mau
SQUASH AND LADYBUG
Private Collection
5609 - 20¾"x18" (53x46 cm)

Hui Chi Mau
PEONIES AND BUTTERFLIES
Private Collection
5608 - 20¾"x18" (53x46 cm)

Shunso Hishida *(Japanese, 1874-1911)*
AZALEA AND PIGEONS
6939 - 23½"x12½" (60x32 cm)

Shunso Hishida
BLACK CAT
6940 - 23½"x12½" (60x32 cm)

Shunso Hishida
MID-AUTUMN
6942 - 23½"x12½" (60x32 cm)

Shunso Hishida
SPRING
6941 - 23½"x12½" (60x32 cm)

Bakusen Tsuchida *(Japanese, 1887-1936)*
CHERRY BLOSSOMS AND PIGEONS
5912 - 15″x16½″ (38x42 cm)

Shiko Imamura *(Japanese, 1880-1916)*
MAGPIE ON A PURPLE WILLOW
5913 - 15″x16½″ (38x42 cm)

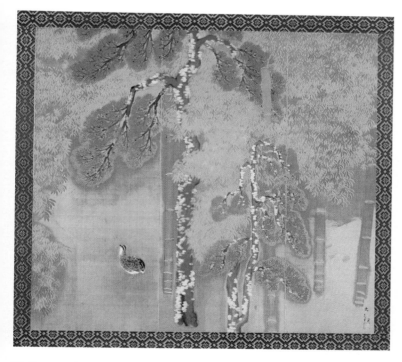

Taikan Yokoyama *(Japanese, 1867-1958)*
PINE TREES AND A QUAIL
5914 - 15″x16½″ (38x42 cm)

Kanzan Shimomura *(Japanese, 1873-1930)*
WHITE FOX
5915 - 15″x16½″ (38x42 cm)

Unknown Chinese Artist (Contemporary)
WISTERIA AND CHICKS
Private Collection
7825 - 24"x28" (61x71 cm)

Hui Chi Mau
AZALEAS AND BUTTERFLIES
Private Collection
5686 - 24"x12" (61x30 cm)

Hui Chi Mau
ROSES IN THE WIND
Private Collection
7349 - 20"x30" (51x76 cm)

Hui Chi Mau
MANY SEASONS
Private Collection
7348 - 20"x30" (51x76 cm)

Hui Chi Mau
FINCHES AND ROSES
Private Collection
5687 - 24"x12" (16x30 cm)

Hui Chi Mau *(Chinese, 1922-   )*
ORIENTAL AUTUMN
Private Collection
5499 - 12"x18" (30½x45½ cm)
7952 - 20"x29¾" (51x76 cm)

Sakai Hoitsu
CHRYSANTHEMUMS
Museum of Fine Arts, Boston
7293 - 29½"x10" (75x25 cm)

Sakai Hoitsu
PEONIES AND CHRYSANTHEMUMS
Museum of Fine Arts, Boston
7294 - 29½"x10" (75x25 cm)

Anonymous Chinese *(12th Century)*
GENTLEMEN GAZING AT A WATERFALL
Private Collection
4519 - 14"x14" (35x35 cm)

Anonymous Chinese *(13th Century)*
BOATS MOORED IN WIND AND RAIN
Private Collection
4516 - 14"x14" (35x35 cm)

Ma Yüan *(Chinese, late 12th to 13th Century)*
PLUM BLOSSOMS BY MOONLIGHT
Private Collection
4518 - 14"x14" (35x35 cm)

Anonymous Chinese *(13th Century)*
EVENING IN THE SPRING HILLS
Private Collection
4517 - 14"x14" (35x35 cm)

Tseng-Ying Pang
MOUNTAIN IN THE MIST, *1966*
Private Collection
8264 - 34½″x15″ (86x38 cm)

Tseng-Ying Pang
LONE TREE, *1966*
Private Collection
8263 - 34½″x15″ (86x38 cm)

Hui-Tsung *(Chinese-Sung
Dynasty Emperor, 1080-1135)*
FINCHES AND BAMBOO
Private Collection
5019 - 11″x18″ (28x46 cm)

Unknown Korean Artist *(Li Dynasty, 17th Century)*
PUPPY CARRYING A PHEASANT FEATHER
Philadelphia Museum of Art
5359 - 14"x17" (35x43 cm)

Unknown Japanese Artist *(14th Century)*
CHIGO DAISHI, THE PRIEST
KOBO DAISHI AS A CHILD (detail)
The Art Institute of Chicago
4201 - 14"x11" (35x27 cm)
8672 - 34"x19" (86x48 cm)

Kano Tannyu *(Japanese, 1602-1674)*
SUMMER PALACE
Private Collection
7295 - 20½"x28" (52x71 cm)

Tsung-Pai Chow *(Chinese, 1820-c. 1875)*
THE POMEGRANATE
Private Collection
5923 - 13½″x24½″ (34x62 cm)

Tzu-Hsiang Chang *(Chinese-Ching Dynasty, 1803-1886)*
APRIL BLOSSOMS
Private Collection
5920 - 13½″x24½″ (34x62 cm)

Tzu-Hsiang Chang
MAY BLOSSOMS
Private Collection
5922 - 13½″x24½″ (34x62 cm)

Tzu-Hsiang Chang
THE IRIS
Private Collection
5921 - 13½″x24½″ (34x62 cm)

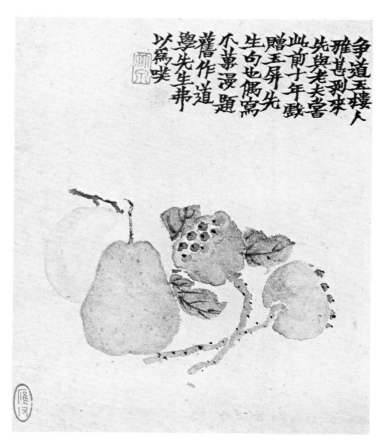

Chin Nung *(Chinese, 1687-1764)*
STILL LIFE—PEAR, APPLE, LOTUS POTS
Private Collection
4625 - 11″x9¼″ (28x23 cm)

Chin Nung
STILL LIFE—WINTER MELON, EGGPLANT, TURNIPS
Private Collection
4626 - 11″x9¼″ (28x23 cm)

Tao-chi *(Chinese, 1641-c. 1720)*
PLUM BLOSSOMS—UNDER THE PINE
Private Collection
4628 - 11¼″x10¼″ (28x26 cm)

Tao-chi
PLUM BLOSSOMS—BY THE SIDE OF BAMBOOS
Private Collection
4627 - 11¼″x10¼″ (28x26 cm)

Wang Yuan-chi *(Chinese, 1642-1715)*
PAVILION WITH DISTANT MOUNTAIN
Alice Boney Collection, New York
5691 - 14″x17″ (35x43 cm)

Wang Yuan-chi
PHILOSOPHER'S RETREAT
Alice Boney Collection, New York
5692 - 14″x17″ (35x43 cm)

Wang Yuan-chi
SNOWSCAPE
Alice Boney Collection, New York
5694 - 14″x17″ (35x43 cm)

Wang Yuan-chi
THE SACRED POND
Alice Boney Collection, New York
5693 - 14″x17″ (35x43 cm)

Tseng-Ying Pang
MOUNTAIN ASCENT
Private Collection
4623 - 16″x12″ (40x30 cm)

Tseng-Ying Pang
CORAL AND BLUE
Private Collection
4624 - 16″x12″ (40x30 cm)

Tseng-Ying Pang
THE LUXURIANCE OF PINE, *1967*
Private Collection
8964 - 31½″x30″ (80x76 cm)

Tseng-Ying Pang
FRAGMENT OF AUTUMN
Private Collection
4621 - 12″x16″ (30x40 cm)

Tseng-Ying Pang, *(Chinese, 1916-   )*
STIRRING LEAVES
Private Collection
4622 - 12″x16″ (30x40 cm)

Japanese, *18th Century*
RED AND WHITE POPPIES
Freer Gallery of Art, Washington, D.C.
7665 - 29¾"x12" (76x30 cm)

Yamamoto Baiitsu
(Japanese, 1783-1856)
HERON AND LOTUS
Milne Henderson Collection, London
8122 - 34"x12" (86x31 cm)

Chugtai
COME FILL THE CUP
7194 - 30″x24″ (76x61 cm)

Chugtai
FOR A SONG
7195 - 30″x24″ (76x61 cm)

Lang Shih-Ning (Giuseppe Castiglione)
(Born: Milan, Italy, 1688 Died; Peking, China, 1766)
AT PASTURE
Shanghai Museum
6781 - 15"x22" (38x56 cm)

Lang Shih-Ning (Giuseppe Castiglione)
(Born: Milan, Italy, 1688 Died: Peking, China, 1766)
PONIES AT PLAY
Shanghai Museum
6782 - 15"x22" (38x56 cm)

Lang Shih-Ning (Giuseppe Castiglione)
(Born: Milan, Italy, 1688 Died: Peking, China, 1766)
TROTTING
Shanghai Museum
6783 - 15"x22" (38x56 cm)

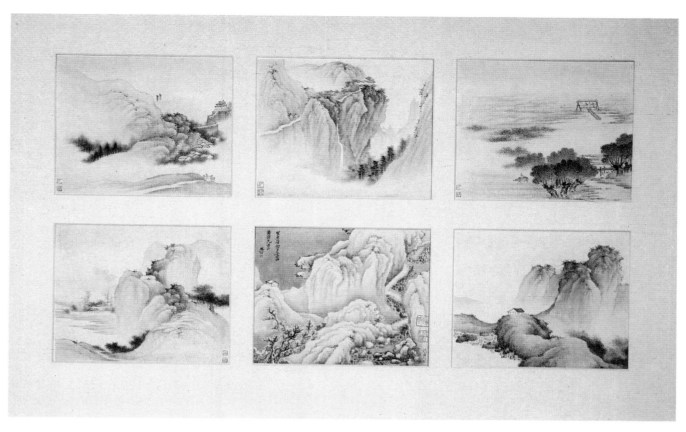

Fan Chi *(Chinese 1616-1694)*
SIX ALBUM LEAVES
Collection of John M. Crawford, Jr.
7646 - 18″x28½″ (45½x72½ cm)

Unknown Chinese Artist *(20th Century)*
TREE PEONIES
Private Collection
9297 - 13½″x38″ (34½x96½ cm)

Unknown Chinese Artist *(Early 19th Century)*
ANCESTOR PORTRAIT
Collection of Toynbee-Clarke Interiors, London
7907 - 30″x22¾″ (76x58 cm)

Unknown Tibetan Artist *(18th Century)*
BODHISATTVA AND OTHER DEITIES
Collection of Mead Art Museum, Amherst College
7298 - 28″x20″ (71x50 cm)

Hovsep Pushman *(Armenian, 1877-1966)*
WHEN AUTUMN IS HERE
University Art Gallery
College of Fine Arts, University of Illinois
6611 - 22½″x15½″ (57x39 cm)

Yeh-lu Ch'u-ts'ai *(Chinese, 1190-1244)*
CALLIGRAPHY, A SEVEN WORD POEM
(Detail of a Handscroll)
Collection of Mr. John M. Crawford, Jr., New York
7197 - 14½"x30" (37x76 cm)

Shiou-Ping Liao *(Chinese, 1936)*
IT'S SPRING AGAIN
Private Collection
8857 - 30"x22½" (76x57 cm)

Tong-Yang Lee *(Chinese-Ming Dynasty, 1447-1516)*
YU YEN TING, c. 1490
Private Collection
9041 - 10"x37" (25x94 cm)

Tseng-Ying Pang
COLD CLOUDS AND WEATHERED TREES
Private Collection
9643 - 36"x27" (91x68 cm)

Attributed to Kano Motonobu *(Japanese, 1456-1559)*
FLOWERS AND BIRDS IN A SPRING LANDSCAPE
The Cleveland Museum of Art
5516 - 18½"x14½" (47x37 cm)
8102 - 30"x24" (76x61 cm)

Henry Wo Yue-kee
LOTUS IN THE RAIN
Private Collection
7076 - 20"x32" (51x81 cm)

ABSTRACT
and
SURREALISM

Nissan Engel, page 420

Elaine Rose (Contemporary American)
NEW HORIZONS, 1985
Courtesy of Elaine Rose Galleries, Houston, Tex.
9986 - 24″x32¼″ (61x81¾ cm)

Elaine Rose (Contemporary American)
THREEFOLD ILLUMINATION, 1984
Private Collection
9996 - 27½″x41½″ (70x105 cm)

Martha Margulis (Contemporary American)
SAND, SKY, WATER II, 1981-82
Collection of the Artist
8136 - 28"x28" (71x71 cm)

Martha Margulis (Contemporary American)
PRIMAVERA
Private Collection
7574 - 18"x30" (45x76 cm)

Lee Burr *(Contemporary American)*
PEDIMENT, *1985*
Courtesy East Park Gallery
9983 - diptych (two panels)
        Each panel 30″x25″ (76x63½ cm)

Lee Burr *(Contemporary American)*
ARCHITRAVE, *1985*
Courtesy of East Park Gallery
8976 - triptych (three panels)
        Each panel 26¼″x22″ (66¾x56 cm)

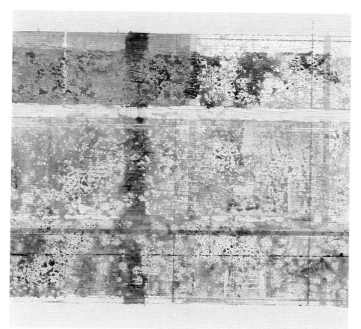

Lee Burr (Contemporary American)
TRANSITIONS, 1985
Courtesy East Park Gallery
8176 - diptych (two panels)
Each panel 24″x24″ (61x61 cm)

Vivian Angel
ODYSSEY, 1985
Private Collection
9984 - 24½″x30″ (62¼x76 cm)

Nissan Engel *(Contemporary French)*
PRELUDE (#6 SWANN), *1984-85*
Private Collection
9849 - 31¾"x23½" (80¾x59½ cm)

David Grant Roth *(Contemporary American)*
ALL DOUBTS SWEPT AWAY, *1984*
Private Collection
8977 - 24"x30" (61x76 cm)

Nissan Engel *(Contemporary French)*
PASTORALE
Private Collection
9985 - 24″x30″ (61x76 cm)

Nissan Engel *(Contemporary French)*
MUSICAL FLIGHT, *1979*
Collection of the Artist
7329 - 21″x31¾″ (53x80 cm)

Marjorie Price *(Contemporary American)*
STRUCTURE IV, *1976*
Private Collection
7980 - 30"x22" (76x56 cm)

Conrad Marca-Relli *(American, 1913-)*
STEEL GREY, *1959-61*
National Collection of Fine Arts
S. C. Johnson Collection
Smithsonian Institution, Washington, D.C.
7712 - 30"x26" (76x66 cm)

Susan Kattas *(Contemporary American)*
HARMONY, *1985*
Private Collection
8156 - 30″x25″ (76x63½ cm)

Sam Francis *(American, 1923-   )*
BLUE OUT OF WHITE, *1958*
Hirshhorn Museum and Sculpture Garden,
Smithsonian Institution
8853 - 26¼″x30¼″ (66x76 cm)

Michael Rossi
KYUSHU, 1978
Private Collection
7755 - 20½″x30″ (52x76 cm)

Michael Rossi *(Contemporary American)*
SPECTRUM SERIES #2, *1984*
Private Collection
7083 - 20″x28″ (50¾x71 cm)

Michael Rossi *(Contemporary American)*
REVERIE
Private Collection
5506 - 18"x14" (46x35 cm)
8606 - 32"x24¾" (81x63 cm)

Michael Rossi *(Contemporary American)*
AUTUMN MIRAGE
Private Collection
7754 - 20½"x30" (52x76 cm)

Mady Daens *(Contemporary Belgian)*
GIANT'S CAUSEWAY, *1980*
Collection of the Artist
7147 - 29¾"x24½" (75½x62 cm)

Mady Daens *(Contemporary Belgian)*
CARNIVAL, *1980*
Private Collection
7146 - 29¾"x24½" (75½x62 cm)

Victor Pasmore *(British, 1908-   )*
SQUARE MOTIF, BLUE AND GOLD:
THE ECLIPSE, *1950*
Tate Gallery, London
6766 - 17¾"x23¾" (45x60 cm)

Robert Motherwell (American, 1915-   )
CAMBRIDGE COLLAGE, 1963
Private Collection
7257 - 28"x19" (71x48 cm)

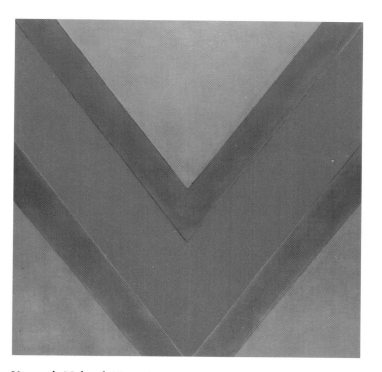

Kenneth Noland (American, 1924-   )
DESERT SOUND, 1963
Hirshhorn Museum and Sculpture Garden, Smithsonian Institution
7144 - 28"x28" (71x71 cm)

Alexander Calder (American, 1898-1976)
HOVERING BOWTIES, 1963
Norton Simon, Inc., New York
8974 - 23"x30¼" (58x76 cm)

Victor Vasarely (Hungarian, 1908-   )
KIU SIU, 1964
Philadelphia Museum of Art
Given by the Friends of the Philadelphia Museum of Art
9978 - 19"x38" (48x96 cm),

Raymond de Botton
BLUE FRAGMENTS *(Alhambra, Granada, Spain), 1969*
Collection of William F. Buckley, Jr., New York
8847 - 30"x23¾" (76x60 cm)

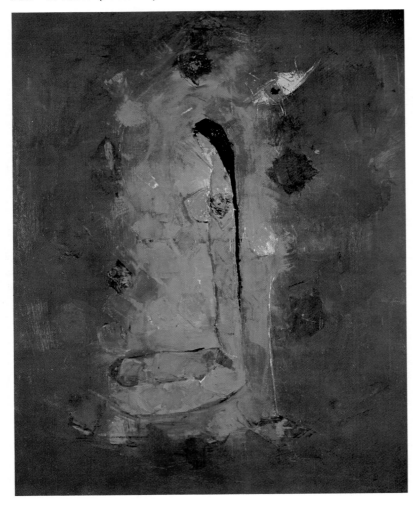

Toby Eric Joysmith *(Contemporary British)*
PALENQUE, *1967*
Collection of Mrs. Carolyn Sammet, Mexico
7877 - 25½″x28″ (64½x71 cm)

Raymond de Botton
THE WHITE HORSE
Collection of William F. Buckley, Jr., New York
8973 - 36″x22½″ (91x57 cm)

Raymond de Botton *(Spanish, 1925-   )*
THE BLUE CAVALIER, *1965*
Collection of William F. Buckley, Jr., New York
9657 - 36″x19″ (91x48 cm)

ABSTRACT & SURREALISM 429

Paul Jenkins *(American, 1923-   )*
SOLSTICE NEAR, *1969*
Private Collection
4617 - 14″x10″ (35x25 cm)

Paul Jenkins
PHENOMENA: CONTINENTAL SHELF 1979
Private Collection
8399 - 24″x30¾″ (61x78 cm)

Paul Jenkins
PHENOMENA: SUN OVER THE HOURGLASS, *1966*
National Collection of Fine Arts
Smithsonian Institution, Washington, D.C.
9547 - 21″x40″ (53x101 cm)

Paul Jenkins
PROMISED RITE, *1969*
Private Collection
4618 - 14″x10″ (35x25 cm)

Paul Jenkins
VEIL BEFORE, *1969*
Private Collection
4620 - 14″x10″ (35x25 cm)

Paul Klee *(Swiss, 1879-1940)*
FISH MAGIC, *c.1925*
Philadelphia Museum of Art
The Louise and Walter Arensberg Collection
7046 - 23½"x30" (59x76 cm)

Paul Klee
PICTURE ALBUM, *1937*
The Phillips Collection, Washington, D.C.
610 - 24"x22½" (60x57 cm)

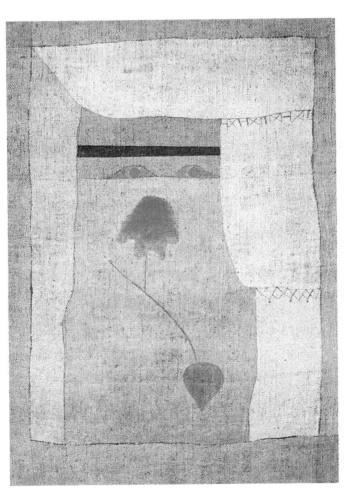

Paul Klee
ARAB SONG, *1932*
The Phillips Collection, Washington, D.C.
7874 - 26"x18" (66x46 cm)

Joan Miró
RED SUN, *1948*
The Phillips Collection, Washington, D.C.
7572 - 28″x22″ (71x56 cm)

Joan Miró *(Spanish, 1893-1983)*
MAN, WOMAN AND CHILD, *1931*
Philadelphia Museum of Art
The Louise and Walter Arensberg Collection
7327 - 23″x30″ (58x76 cm)

Max Ernst *(German, 1891-1976)*
LE VENT SE REPOSE JAUNE, *1952*
Acquavella Galleries, Inc., New York
6442 - 25½″x21″ (65x53½ cm)

Arthur Secunda
DISTANT MOUNTAIN, *1976*
Private Collection
6315 - 24″x18″ (61x46 cm)

Arthur Secunda
CHROMATIC SQUARE
Private Collection
5354 - 23″x24″ (59x61 cm)

Piet Mondrian
OPPOSITION OF LINES, RED AND YELLOW, *1937*
Philadelphia Museum of Art
A. E. Gallatin Collection
5098 - 21″x17¼″ (43x33 cm)

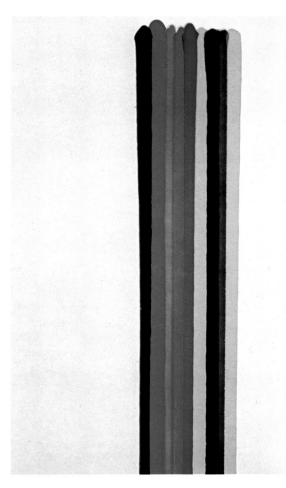

Hans Hofmann *(American, 1881-1966)*
VELUTI IN SPECULUM, *1962*
The Metropolitan Museum of Art, New York
Gift of Mr. and Mrs. Richard Rogers
and Francis Lathrop Fund, 1963
7313 - 28″x24″ (71x61 cm)

Morris Louis *(American, 1912-1962)*
COLOR LINE, *1961*
Hirshhorn Museum and Sculpture Garden,
Smithsonian Institution
8852 - 34¼″x20″ (86x50 cm)

Thomas Lloyd Ramsier *(American, 1927-   )*
MAKAHA VALLEY, HAWAII
Private Collection
9660 - 30″x40″ (76x101 cm)

Gregorio Prestopino *(American, 1907-   )*
FALL LANDSCAPE WITH FOUR TREES
National Collection of Fine Arts
Smithsonian Institution, Washington, D.C.
9632 - 32¾″x28″ (83x71 cm)

Wassily Kandinsky *(Russian, 1866-1944)*
HEAVY CIRCLES, *1927*
The Blue Four Galka Scheyer Collection
Norton Simon Museum, Pasadena
6529 - 24″x22″ (61x55½ cm)

Arthur Dove *(American, 1880-1946)*
ABSTRACT, THE FLOUR MILL, *1938*
The Phillips Collection, Washington, D.C.
7272 - 26″x15¾″ (66x40 cm)

Wassily Kandinsky *(Russian, 1866-1944)*
COMPOSITION, *1934*
Stedelijk Museum, Amsterdam
6920 - 17½″x23″ (44x58 cm)

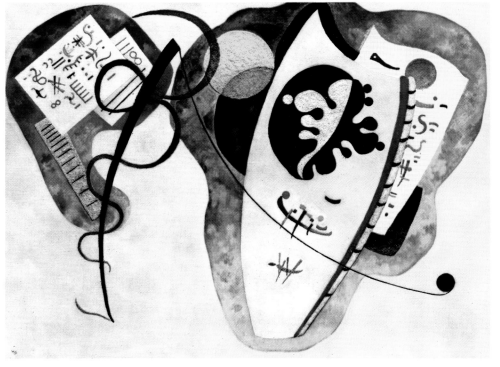

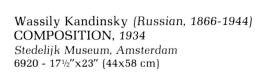

Helen Struven *(Contemporary American)*
MINGLED FORMS
Collection of the Artist
7844 - 28"x22" (71x56 cm)

Marcel Duchamp *(French, 1887-1968)*
NUDE DESCENDING A STAIRCASE, *Number 2, 1912*
Philadelphia Museum of Art
7047 - 30"x18" (76x45 cm)

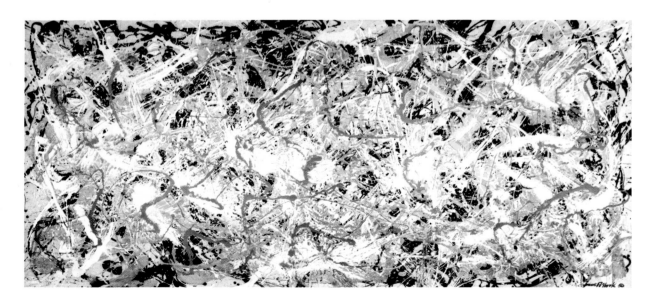

Jackson Pollock *(American, 1912-1956)*
NUMBER 27, *1950*
Whitney Museum of American Art, New York
7057 - 13½"x29½" (34x75 cm)

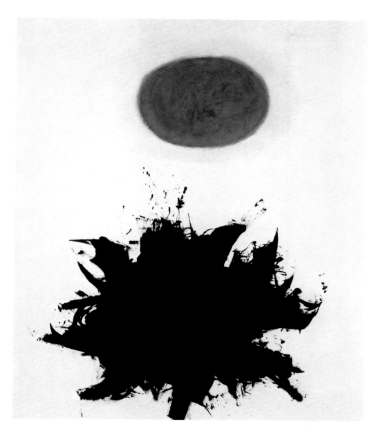

Adolph Gottlieb (American, 1903-1974)
THRUST, 1959
The Metropolitan Museum of Art, New York
George A. Hearn Fund, 1959
7314 - 28"x23¼" (71x59 cm)

Leonard Brooks (Contemporary Canadian)
TIME PENDULUM
Collection of the Artist
9980 - 32"x23½" (81x60 cm)

Clyfford Still (American, 1904-1980)
1957-D, No. 1, 1957
Albright-Knox Art Gallery, Buffalo, New York
Gift of Seymour H. Knox
8970 - 23¾"x33¾" (60x85 cm)

Lyonel Feininger
BLUE MARINE, 1924
Munson-Williams-Proctor Institute, Utica
8000 - 18″x32″ (46x81 cm)

Lyonel Feininger *(American, 1871-1956)*
BIRD CLOUD, 1926
Busch-Reisinger Museum
of Germanic Culture
Harvard University
7928 - 17¼″x28″ (44x71 cm)

440   ABSTRACT & SURREALISM

Ben Shahn *(American, 1898-1969)*
ALLEGORY, *1948*
Fort Worth Art Museum
6051 - 21″x28″ (53x71 cm)

Stanton Macdonald-Wright *(American, 1890-1973)*
CANON SYNCHRONY, *c. 1919*
University Gallery, University of Minnesota, Minneapolis
7382 - 25″x25″ (63x63 cm)

Seymour Fogel *(Contemporary American)*
COMPLEX WITH RED, *1978*
Collection of the Artist
8118 - 22½″x30″ (57x76 cm)

ABSTRACT & SURREALISM 441

Salvador Dalí
THE MADONNA OF PORT LLIGAT, *1950*
Private Collection
4505 - 14″x10½″ (35x26 cm)
7280 - 28″x21″ (71x53 cm)

Salvador Dalí
DISCOVERY OF AMERICA BY
CHRISTOPHER COLUMBUS, *1959*
Collection Mr. and Mrs. A. Reynolds Morse
Loaned to the Dali Museum, Cleveland, Ohio
7692 - 28″x21″ (71x53 cm)

Salvador Dalí
COMPOSITION, *1942*
Private Collection
6087 - 22″x25½″ (56x65 cm)

René Magritte *(Belgian, 1898-1967)*
THE TEMPEST, *undated*
Wadsworth Atheneum, Hartford
6356 - 19¼″x25½″ (48x64 cm)

Leonor Fini
MELITA, *1961*
Private Collection
7559 - 31″x10″ (80x25 cm)

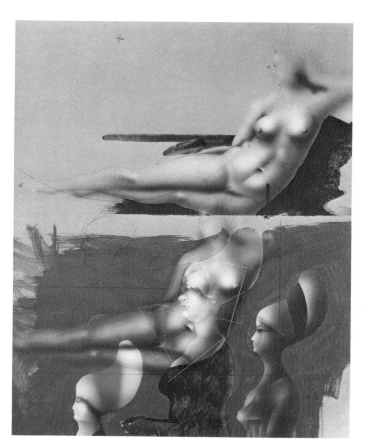

Paul Wunderlich *(German, 1927-   )*
ZU A.D.
Private Collection
6526 - 26″x20½″ (66x52 cm)

ABSTRACT & SURREALISM 443

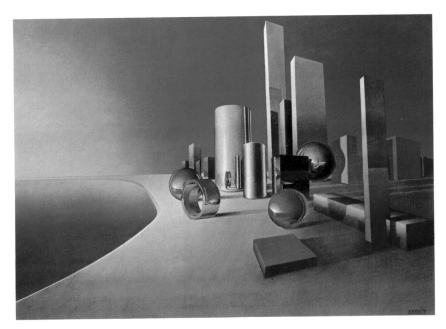

Ralph Hertle *(American, 1937-   )*
UNTIL NOW
Private Collection
9062 - 24″x32″ (61x81 cm)

Ralph Hertle
DYNAMIS
Collection of Mr. Gary Steen, Los Angeles, Calif.
9070 - 21½″x36″ (54x91 cm)

WESTERN
and
SOUTHWESTERN

Georgia O'Keeffe,   page 457

Frederic Remington
ATTACK ON THE SUPPLY WAGONS
Private Collection
5357 - 16"x24" (40x61 cm)

Frederic Remington
ARGUMENT WITH THE TOWN MARSHAL
Private Collection
5356 - 16"x24" (40x61 cm)

Charles Marion Russell
(American, 1865-1926)
THE WORLD WAS ALL BEFORE THEM
C. R. Smith Collection, New York City
6522 - 18¾"x28" (47x71 cm)
9098 - 24"x36" (61x91 cm)

3415 - THE FIGHT FOR THE WATER HOLE

3416 - THE FLIGHT

Frederic Remington *(American, 1861-1909)*
WESTERN SCENES
Museum of Fine Arts of Houston
3412-17 - each 8″x12″ (20x30 cm)

3417 - NEW YEAR ON THE CIMARRON

3412 - AIDING A COMRADE

3413 - CHANGE OF OWNERSHIP

3414 - THE EMIGRANTS
7252 - 17½"x26" (44x66 cm)

Alfred Jacob Miller *(American, 1810-1874)*
INDIAN SCOUT, *1851*
Denver Public Library
6016 - 18″x24¼″ (46x61 cm)

E. Irving Couse *(American)*
WATCHING FOR GAME
Collection of the Phoenix Art Museum
6100 - 22″x26½″ (56x67 cm)

William R. Leigh
BULL DIVING
6721 - 22″x18″ (56x46 cm)

William R. Leigh
BULL DOGGING
6722 - 22″x18″ (56x46 cm)

William R. Leigh *(American, 1866-1955)*
DOUBLE CROSSER
6723 - 22″x18″ (56x46 cm)

William R. Leigh
GREASED LIGHTNING
6724 - 22″x18″ (56x46 cm)

Peter Hurd *(American, 1904-   )*
RANCHERIA, *1938*
The Metropolitan Museum of Art, New York
6242 - 12"x22" (30x56 cm)

Lon Megargee *(American, dates unknown)*
HOME ON THE RANCH
5932 - 16"x20" (40x51 cm)

3011 - WILD HORSE RANCH

3012 - POPPIES AND MOMMIES

3013 - DEER AT WATER HOLE

3014 - LOST AND FOUND

3015 - SILVER CREEK

3016 - SUMMER STORM

Ray Strang
WESTERN SCENES
Series 3011-16 - each 7½″x10″ (19x25 cm)

Blackbear Bosin *(American, 1921-   )*
PRAIRIE FIRE
Philbrook Art Center, Tulsa, Okla.
7948 - 18½"x30" (47x76 cm)

Velino Shije Herrera *(American)*
BUFFALO HUNT
The University of Arizona Museum of Art Collection
7676 - 18"x25¼" (46x65 cm)

Georgia O'Keeffe *(American, 1887-1986)*
WHITE CANADIAN BARN, NO. 2, *1932*
The Metropolitan Museum of Art, New York
Alfred Stieglitz Collection
8271 - 12″x30″ (30x76 cm)

Georgia O'Keeffe
RAM'S HEAD, WHITE HOLLYHOCK
AND LITTLE HILLS, *1935*
Edith and Milton Lowenthal Collection, New York
7025 - 25″x30″ (63x76 cm)

ANIMALS

Travis Keese,   page 465

Jean-Léon Gérôme (French, 1824-1904)
THE TWO MAJESTIES, 1883
Milwaukee Art Center, Layton Art Collection
7982 - 16¼"x30" (41x76 cm)

Arthur F. Tait (American, 1819-1905)
ALERT
Brigham Young University
7538 - 18"x30" (46x76 cm)

Carl Clemens Moritz Rungius *(German, 1869-1959)*
PRONGHORN ANTELOPE
New York Zoological Society
8845 - 24″x30″ (60x76 cm)

A. Radclyffe Dugmore *(British, 1870-?)*
WATERHOLE NORTHERN KENYA,
1925
New York Zoological Society
9052 - 24″x36″ (60x91 cm)

Carl Clemens Moritz Rungius
PUMA
New York Zoological Society
8846 - 24″x30″ (60x76 cm)

Henry Wo Yue-kee (Chinese, 1927-   )
TWO TIGERS
Collection of the Artist
5508 - 11"x18" (28x46 cm)
9066 - 22¼"x36" (57x91 cm)

Paul O. Longenecker (Contemporary American)
PAIR OF CHEETAHS
Private Collection
7847 - 22"x28" (56x70 cm)

Milton Avery
FRENCH PIGEONS
Private Collection, New York
7201 - 21″x28″ (53x71 cm)

Roland Chenard *(Contemporary Canadian)*
FULL FLIGHT, *1979*
Collection of the Artist
6943 - 18″x28⅛″ (46x71 cm)

Travis Keese *(American, 1932-   )*
WILD TURKEY
Private Collection
7941 - 20″x30″ (51x76 cm)

Travis Keese
WHITE TAIL DEER
Private Collection
7942 - 20″x30″ (51x76 cm)

Robert Ravelle
UP A TREE, *1970*
Private Collection
6400 - 20″x24″ (50x60 cm)

Robert Ravelle *(German, 1918-   )*
FRIEND OR FOE?, *1970*
Private Collection
6401 - 20″x24″ (50x60 cm)

Shirley Howe *(Contemporary American)*
RED SQUIRREL WITH YELLOW PRIMROSES
Private Collection
2761 - 5"x7" (13x18 cm)

Shirley Howe
CHIPMUNK WITH BLUEBERRIES
Private Collection
2760 - 5"x7" (13x18 cm)

Shirley Howe
RABBIT WITH NASTURTIUMS
Private Collection
3750 - 8"x10" (20x26 cm)

Nan Lee
THEY SHALL DWELL TOGETHER
Private Collection
7679 - 22"x26" (56x66 cm)

Hsien-Min Yang (*Contemporary Chinese*)
PANDAS AT PLAY
Private Collection
5556 - 16"x20" (41x51 cm)

Nan Lee (*American, 1920-   *)
THE PEACEABLE KINGDOM
Private Collection
5518 - 14½"x14½" (37x37 cm)
6515 - 24"x24" (61x61 cm)

Giacomo Balla *(Italian, 1874-1958)*
DOG ON A LEASH, *1912*
George F. Goodyear and
The Buffalo Fine Arts Academy
7306 - 23"x28" (58x71 cm)

John Marin
CIRCUS ELEPHANTS, *1941*
The Art Institute of Chicago
787 - 19"x24" (48x61 cm)

Ida Pellei
THE LEOPARDS
Private Collection
8950 - 24″x29¾″ (61x76 cm)

Dan Poole *(American, 1942-   )*
ZEBRA
Private Collection
7996 - 26″x17″ (66x43 cm)

Mara Abboud *(Contemporary American)*
THREE ZEBRAS
Private Collection
8864 - 30¼″x24″ (77x61 cm)

Gene Pelham *(American, 1915-)*
NOI, *1967*
Private Collection
5546 - 14½″x13½″ (37x34 cm)
7343 - 28″x26″ (71x66 cm)

Jessie Arms Botke *(American, 1883-)*
TROPICAL POOL
8340 - 24″x32″ (61x83 cm)

Cynthia Augeri *(American, 1946-   )*
GRAY SQUIRREL
Private Collection
6938 - 26″x20″ (66x51 cm)

Albrecht Dürer
THE LITTLE OWL, *1508*
3740 - 7½″x5½″ (18x13 cm)

Bruce Lattig *(American, 1933-   )*
GREAT HORNED OWL, *1970*
Private Collection
5539 - 18″x12¾″ (46x32 cm)
6520 - 28″x20″ (71x51 cm)

Miguel Ibarz Roca *(Spanish, 1920-   )*
SPRING SONG, *1965*
Private Collection
7316 - 23½″x30″ (59x76 cm)

Anthony La Paglia *(American, active 1952)*
BLUE-JAY
6366 - 22½″x18½″ (57x47 cm)

Anthony La Paglia
CARDINAL
6365 - 22½″x18½″ (57x47 cm)

John James Audubon
PILEATED WOODPECKER, 1825
From Birds of America, folio edition
7648 - 30"x19½" (76x50 cm)

John James Audubon
SUMMER OR WOOD DUCK, 1825
From Birds of America, folio edition
7650 - 30"x19½" (76x50 cm)

Additional Audubon Birds,
See Poster Section Page 529

6368
YELLOW-BREASTED CHAT

John James Audubon *(American, 1785-1851)*
AUDUBON BIRD SERIES
21"x17" (53x43 cm)

6369
RUBY-THROATED
HUMMING BIRD

6367
COMMON GROSSBILL

BLUE-JAY
4954 - 16″x12″ (40x30 cm)
6954 - 24½″x19½″ (62x49 cm)

RED-CAPPED FRUIT DOVE
4960 - 16″x12″ (40x30 cm)

Cecil Golding
BIRD SERIES

BLOSSOM-HEADED PARAKEET
4955 - 16″x12″ (40x30 cm)
6955 - 24½″x19½″ (62x49 cm)

RED-SHAFTED FLICKER
4951 - 16″x12″ (40x30 cm)

Robert Wesley Amick
MAN O'WAR
4700 - 11"x14" (27x35 cm)
7700 - 19¾"x26" (50x66 cm)

George Ford Morris
WHIRLAWAY (A Study)
5372 - 17"x13" (43x33 cm)

George Ford Morris *(American, 1877-1961)*
MAN O'WAR (A Study)
5371 - 17"x13" (43x33 cm)

Sam Savitt *(Contemporary American)*
MALACCA, 1969
Collection of Mrs. Oliver D. Appleton
6870 - 19¾"x25½" (50x69 cm)

George Ford Morris
WHIRLAWAY
4340 - 9½"x12½" (24x31 cm)

Robert Wesley Amick *(American, 1879-1969)*
BLACK STALLION, *undated*
Wilmot E. Forbes Collection
7904 - 22½″x30″ (57x76 cm)

Ray Strang *(American, 1893-1954)*
PLAYMATES
2574 - 7½″x6″ (19x15 cm)
4574 - 14″x11″ (35x28 cm)

Ray Strang
CURIOSITY
2575 - 7½″x6″ (19x15 cm)
4575 - 14″x11″ (35x28 cm)

Ricardo Arenys
ON THE RANGE
Private Collection
9049 - 16¼″x39¾″ (41x101 cm)

Ricardo Arenys
HORSES IN THE FOOTHILLS
Private Collection
7137 - 22¾"x30" (57x76 cm)

Ricardo Arenys *(Spanish, 1914-   )*
THOROUGHBREDS, *1964*
Private Collection
7141 - 21"x30" (53x76 cm)

Ricardo Arenys
IN THE PASTURE, *1963*
Private Collection
9048 - 16¼"x39¾" (41x101 cm)

Ricardo Arenys
WHITE THOROUGHBREDS, *1965*
Private Collection
4605 - 14″x10¼″ (35x26 cm)
8046 - 31½″x23″ (80x58 cm)

Ricardo Arenys
WHITE HORSES, *1962*
Private Collection
4604 - 14″x10¼″ (35x26 cm)
8047 - 31½″x23″ (80x58 cm)

Ricardo Arenys
HORSES AGAINST A BLUE BACKGROUND, *1966*
Private Collection
8272 - 31½″x23½″ (78x59 cm)

Nissan Engel *(French, 1931-   )*
EL PICADOR, *1961*
Alfred Reyn Galleries, New York
7799 - 21″x29¾″ (53x75 cm)

Nissan Engel
HORSEMAN, *1970*
Private Collection
7716 - 28″x21¾″ (71x55 cm)

Nissan Engel
DON QUIXOTE
Private Collection
7801 - 28″x21″ (71x53 cm)

MASTER DRAWINGS

MINIATURES

SCULPTURE
and
ARTIFACTS

U.N.E.S.C.O.

URBAN SCENES

Francesco Guardi *(Italian, 1712-1793)*
THE GRAND CANAL BEYOND RIALTO
3637 - 10″x9½″ (25x24 cm)

Tuscan, *Early 15th Century*
ANIMALS AND GROUPS OF ANIMALS
3642 - 9″x6¾″ (22x17 cm)

MASTERPIECES OF ITALIAN DRAWING

IN THE

ALBERTINA COLLECTION

Donato Creti *(Italian, 1671-1749)*
THE ASTRONOMERS
The Art Institute of Chicago
3038 - 7½″x10″ (19x25 cm)

Paolo Veronese *(Italian, 1530-1588)*
PASTORAL LANDSCAPE
WITH FLOCK AND SHEPHERDESS
3643 - 6½″x9¾″ (16x24 cm)

Ubaldo Gandolfi *(Italian, 1728-1781)*
A BOY'S HEAD
3636 - 11¼"x8" (28x20 cm)

Pietro da Cortona *(Italian, 1596-1669)*
YOUNG WOMAN'S HEAD
3632-11"x8¼" (28x21 cm)

Annibale Carracci *(Italian, 1560-1609)*
NUDE STUDY OF A YOUNG MAN
3630 - 8¼"x9¾" (21x24 cm)

Michelangelo Buonarroti *(Italian, 1475-1564)*
MALE NUDE, BACK VIEW
3639 - 7¼"x9¾" (18x24 cm)

Alessio De Marchis *(Italian, 1684-1752)*
RIVERSIDE SCENE WITH A HERD OF COWS
3635 - 6″x9¾″ (15x24 cm)

Guercino (G.F. Barbieri)
ST. DOMENICUS KNEELING
BEFORE MADONNA AND CHILD
3638 - 10½″x8″ (26x20 cm)

Guercino (G.F. Barbieri) *(Italian, 1591-1666)*
SUSANNA AND THE ELDERS
Ambrosiana Gallery, Milan
4162 - 11½″x10½″ (29x26 cm)

Michelangelo Buonarroti *(Italian, 1475-1564)*
MADONNA AND CHILD, *c. 1512*
Casa Buonarroti, Florence
6390 - 21¼″x15½″ (54x39 cm)

Michelangelo Buonarroti
EPIPHANY, *c. 1550*
The British Museum, London
The Malcolm Collection
6391 - 21¼″x15½″ (54x36 cm)

Jean Auguste Dominique Ingres
PORTRAIT OF CHARLES GOUNOD, *1841*
The Art Institute of Chicago
3037 - 11¾"x9" (30x23 cm)

Francisco de Goya *(Spanish, 1746-1828)*
BE CAREFUL WITH THAT STEP, *1810-19*
The Art Institute of Chicago
3047 - 12"x8" (30x20 cm)

Jean Auguste Dominique Ingres
PORTRAIT OF MME. CHARLES GOUNOD, 1855
The Art Institute of Chicago
3036 - 11¾"x9" (30x23 cm)

3430 - A HAPPY DISCOVERY

3431 - THE LAST TRY

Honoré Daumier
TWO MEDICAL SKETCHES
3430-31 approx. 6″x7″ (15x17 cm)

3404 - PLEAD NOT GUILTY

3405 - SO GOES HIS STORY

3406 - THIS SAINTLY WOMAN

Honoré Daumier
SIX LEGAL SKETCHES
3404-09 approx. 9″x8″ (22x20 cm)

3407 - SUCH A DEVOTED
HUSBAND

3408 - A SURE CASE

3409 - A RESPECTED CITIZEN

3121 - Daffinger
AGE OF INNOCENCE

3109 - Daffinger
MADAME DAFFINGER

PORTRAITS

Average plate size
11″x9″ (28x22 cm)

3111 - Peter
HUNGARIAN COUNTESS

3117 - Lequeutre
FRENCH PRINCESS

3116 - Kobel
COMTESSE D'ORSAY

3113 - Saar
LILAC TIME

3114 - Unknown Artist
GIRL IN BLUE

3115 - Saar
LADY IN ORCHID

Various Artists
JEWELS OF MINIATURE PAINTING
7200 - 5"x4" (12x10 cm) Sheet of 20

Greek, *c. 150 B.C.*
VENUS DE MILO (APHRODITE OF MELOS)
Louvre Museum, Paris
9570 - 37½"x13½" (95x34 cm)

Etruscan, *c. 475 B.C.*
MUSICIANS
Tomb of the Leopards, Tarquinia
8014 - 15"x30½" (38x77 cm)

Babylonian, Reign of Nebuchadnezzar II, 604-562 B.C.
THE DRAGON OF BEL-MARDUK (Detail from the Ishtar Gate)
Detroit Institute of the Arts
Gift of the Founders Society, General Membership Fund, 1931
7482 - 20"x29¾" (52x76 cm)

Egyptian, XXII Dynasty, 950-c.730 B.C.
QUEEN KAROMANA, WIFE OF
THELETH II
Louvre Museum, Paris
9630 - 37¼"x16" (94x40 cm)

Egyptian, XVIII Dynasty, 14th Century B.C.
GOLDEN EFFIGY OF KING TUTANKHAMEN
Cairo Museum
6836 - 21½"x18¾" (54x47 cm)

SCULPTURE & ARTIFACTS   493

UNITED NATIONS EDUCATIONAL, SCIENTIFIC AND CULTURAL ORGANIZATION REPRODUCTIONS

U.N.E.S.C.O. series is "designed to bring within the reach of artists, teachers, students and the wide art-loving public the finest quality color reproductions of masterpieces of art which hitherto have been known to a limited few."

Average picture is about 14″ x 11″ (35x28 cm). Paper size is standard 18¾″ x 13¼″ (47½x33½ cm).

The following are examples of the large variety of images within this series. If you would like to have the complete listing of over 150 reproductions representing more than 20 countries, please contact us directly.

1584 - INDIA

1646 - U.S.S.R.

1636 - U.S.S.R.

1572 - JAPAN   1570 - JAPAN   1571 - JAPAN

1626 - TURKEY

1527 - EGYPT

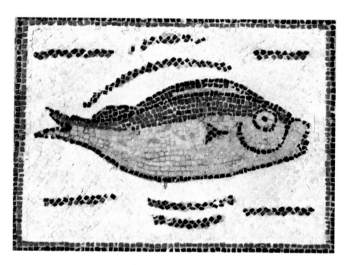

1617 - TUNISIA

1547 - IRAN

1543 - IRAN

1544 - IRAN

Oskar Kokoschka *(Austrian, 1886-1980)*
NEW YORK, *1966*
Collection of Mr. and Mrs. John Mosler, New York
9644 - 26¾"x36" (68x91 cm)

George Grosz *(American, 1893-1959)*
MANHATTAN HARBOR
Private Collection
6068 - 22"x16½" (56x42 cm)

Maurice Utrillo
RUE A SANNOIS
Private Collection
4281 - 11"x14" (28x35 cm)
5281 - 13"x20" (32x50 cm)

Maurice Utrillo
MAISON MIMI, *1936*
Private Collection
4030 - 11"x14" (28x35 cm)
6030 - 19½"x24" (50x60 cm)

Maurice Utrillo
PETIT CAFE, MONTMARTRE
Private Collection
4282 - 11"x14" (28x35 cm)
5282 - 13"x20" (32x50 cm)

Frans Van Lamsweerde *(Dutch, 1924-1969)*
WATERFRONT, *1968*
Private Collection
5249 - 15¼"x20" (38x50 cm)
9649 - 28"x36¾" (71x93 cm)

Frans Van Lamsweerde
PORT O'CALL, *1967*
Private Collection
5247 - 15¼"x20" (38x50 cm)

Frans Van Lamsweerde
RUSTIC GLEN, *1969*
Private Collection
9668 - 27½"x36" (69x91 cm)

Frans Van Lamsweerde
MEDITERRANEAN FANTASY, *1969*
Private Collection
5246 - 20"x15¼" (58x38 cm)
9667 - 36"x27½" (91x69 cm)

Frans Van Lamsweerde
THE TOURNAMENT, *1969*
Private Collection
5248 - 20"x15¼" (50x38 cm)
9669 - 36"x27½" (91x69 cm)

John Wheat *(American, 1920-   )*
DREAMS AND SHADOWS, *1970*
Private Collection
9974 - 18¾"x37¾" (47x95 cm)

William Thon
TWILIGHT IN ROME, *1961*
National Collection of Fine Arts
S. C. Johnson Collection
Smithsonian Institution, Washington, D.C.
9565 - 24"x40" (61x101 cm)

Lyonel Feininger
GOTHIC GABLES
The Joseph H. Hirshhorn Collection
6225 - 14¼"x24" (37x61 cm)

POSTERS

Ann Taylor,   page 521

503

Edward Hopper
GROUND SWELL
30190 - 28¼"x30" (71¾x76 cm)

Georges Seurat
PORT EN BESSIN: THE OUTER HARBOR (LOW TIDE)
30206 - 32"x30" (81x76 cm)

Edward Hopper
STREET SCENE, GLOUCESTER
30186 - 28"x30" (71x76 cm)

Pierre Auguste Renoir
THE SEINE AT ARGENTEUIL
30200 - 28¼"x30½" (71¾x77½ cm)

John H. Twachtman
SPRINGTIME
30185 - 25"x30" (63½x76 cm)

Gustave Caillebotte
PERISSOIRES SUR L'YERRES
30171 - 26"x34" (66x86½ cm)

Claude Monet
THE SEINE AT GIVERNY, MORNING MIST
30201 - 34"x26" (86½x66 cm)

Mary Cassatt
SLEEPY BABY
30179 - 36"x24" (91½x61 cm)

Claude Monet
GLADIOLI
30204 - 26"x29¾" (66x75½ cm)

Charles Ebert
FISHERMAN'S HUT
30205 - 32"x26" (81x66 cm)

Frederick Carl Frieseke
THE GARDEN PARASOL
30202 - 31½"x28" (80x71 cm)

William Chadwick
IRISES
30208 - 30"x26" (76x66 cm)

Frank Weston Benson
EVENING LIGHT
30187 - 30"x25" (76x63½ cm)

William Merritt Chase
NEAR THE BEACH, SHINNECOCK
30196 - 26"x30" (66x76 cm)

David Maitland Armstrong
THE BAR, BAR HARBOR, MT. DESERT
30173 - 25"x36" (63½x91½ cm)

Winslow Homer
THE FOUR LEAF CLOVER
30203 - 28"x30" (71x76 cm)

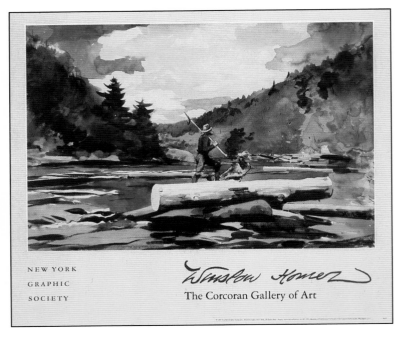

Winslow Homer
THE HUDSON RIVER—LOGGING
30191 - 26"x30" (66x76 cm)

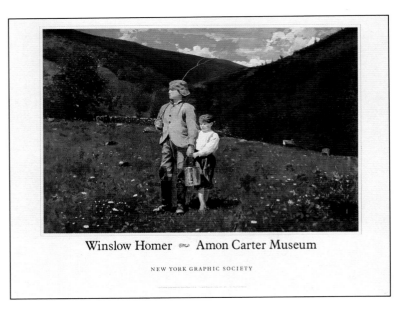

Winslow Homer
CROSSING THE PASTURE
30207 - 27¼"x34" (69¼x86½ cm)

Childe Hassam
RIALTO MARKET, VENICE
30198 - 36"x23¾" (91½x60 cm)

Childe Hassam
FLAGS ON THE FRIAR'S CLUB
30209 - 30"x24" (76x61 cm)

Childe Hassam
RAINY DAY, BOSTON
30197 - 24"x36" (61x91½ cm)

Daniel Ridgeway Knight
AN IDLE MOMENT
30172 - 26"x26" (66x66 cm)

Louis Comfort Tiffany
AT IRVINGTON-ON-HUDSON
30038 - 26"x30" (66x76 cm)

Unknown American Artist
LYDIA AND TABITHA
30188 - 36"x24" (91½x61 cm)

Jan van Os
FLOWERS
30170 - 32"x21" (81x53½ cm)

Flour Mill
Andrew Wyeth

New York Graphic Society

Copyright © Andrew Wyeth
Andrew Wyeth
FLOUR MILL
30192 - 36″x24″ (91½x61 cm)

The Art of

New York Graphic Society

Copyright © Andrew Wyeth
Andrew Wyeth
GROUND WIRE
30193 - 27¼″x27¼″ (69¼x69¼ cm)

Sakai Hoitsu
IRIS AND MANDARIN DUCKS
30011 - 38½"x19" (97¾x48¼ cm)

Tosa Mitsuoki
QUAILS AND FLOWERS
30008 - 24"x20" (61x50¾ cm)

Yun Shou-p'ing
ROSES AND IRIS
30005 - 25"x22" (63½x56 cm)

Unknown Chinese Artist
CAMELLIA FESTIVAL
30017 - 16"x30" (40½x76 cm)

Regan Melone
CHABANA
30181 - 26"x38" (66x96½ cm)

Hieronymus Bosch
THE GARDEN OF DELIGHTS
30009 - 29½″x39¼″ (75x99½ cm)

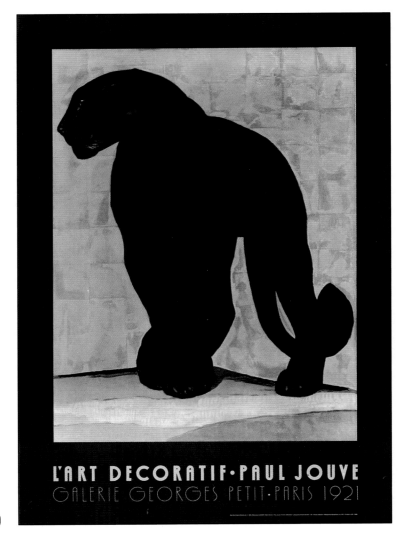

Paul Jouve
BLACK PANTHER
30006 - 39″x28″ (99x71 cm)

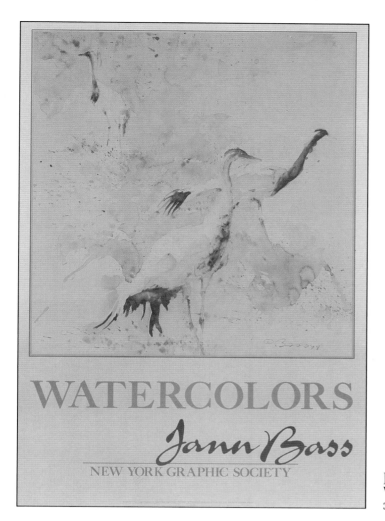

Jann T. Bass
WITHERWARD
30155 - 37¼"x26" (94½x66 cm)

Sakai Hoitsu
CRANES
30012 - 40"x30" (101½x76 cm)

The Complete Ansel Adams Collection

MOONRISE, HERNANDEZ
20002 - 36″x25½″ (91½x64¾ cm)

MOON OVER HALF DOME
20177 - 36″x25½″ (91½x64¾ cm)

MT. McKINLEY AND WONDER LAKE
20176 - 36″x25½″ (91½x64¾ cm)

OAK TREE, SNOWSTORM
20138 - 36″x25½″ (91½x64¾ cm)

ASPENS
20003 - 36″x25½″ (91½x64¾ cm)

SAND DUNES
20175 - 36″x25½″ (91½x64¾ cm)

The New Ansel Adams Photography Series

WINTER SUNRISE, SIERRA NEVADA
20082 - 25½"x28¾" (64¾x73 cm)

ANSEL ADAMS · EXAMPLES

MT. WILLIAMSON
20139 - 25½"x29" (64¾x73½ cm)

ANSEL ADAMS · THE PRINT

FROZEN LAKE AND CLIFFS
20080 - 25½"x28¾" (64½x73 cm)

The Portfolios of Ansel Adams

MONOLITH, THE FACE OF HALF DOME
20081 - 36"x25½" (91½x65 cm)

Ansel Adams · The Print

LEAVES, MT. RANIER
20137 - 36"x25½" (91½x64¾ cm)

ANSEL ADAMS

Yosemite and the Range of Light

CLEARING WINTER STORM
20001 - 36"x25½" (91½x64¾ cm)

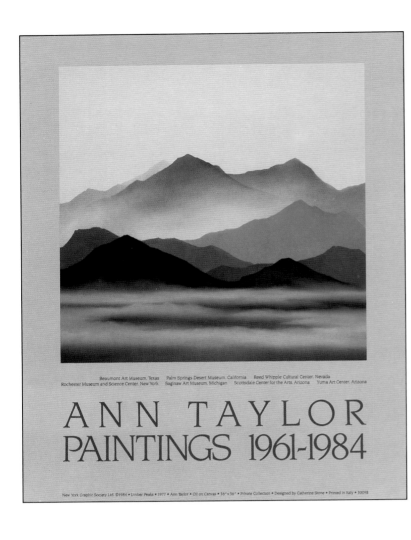

Ann Taylor
UMBER PEAKS
30098 - 30"x23½" (76x59½ cm)

Ann Taylor
PRESTWICK DEPARTURE
30184 - 36"x24" (91½x61 cm)

Ann Taylor
MARY'S MESAS
30160 - 30"x36" (76x91½ cm)

Ann Taylor
LINGERING BELOW
30015 - 29½"x39" (75x99 cm)

Marianne Hornbuckle
BIG BEND
30132 - 26"x30½" (66x77½ cm)

Sam Scopas
TAOS PUEBLO
30134 - 36"x24" (91½x61 cm)

Dolona Roberts
STRIPED BLANKETS
30133 - 25"x33½" (63½x85 cm)

INDIAN IMAGES

Southwest Series

Roland Reed
Photographer (1864–1934)

New York Graphic Society

Roland Reed
THE POTTERY MAKER
30146 - 36″x24″ (91½x61 cm)

IMAGES OF THE PLAINS

Roland Reed 1864–1934

NEW YORK GRAPHIC SOCIETY

Roland Reed
THE COUNCIL
30145 - 36″x24″ (91½x61 cm)

Virgil Thrasher
NORTHERN AND CENTRAL CALIFORNIA LANDSCAPES
20084 - 36"x24" (91½x61 cm)

Virgil Thrasher
CALIFORNIA LANDSCAPES
20083 - 24"x36" (61x91½ cm)

Virgil Thrasher
BLACK MOUNTAIN
30016 - 25"x30" (63½x76 cm)

Virgil Thrasher
LAKE TAHOE
30199 - 28"x24" (71x61 cm)

Ken Davies
BUTTER CHURN
30131 - 36"x20" (91½x50¾ cm)

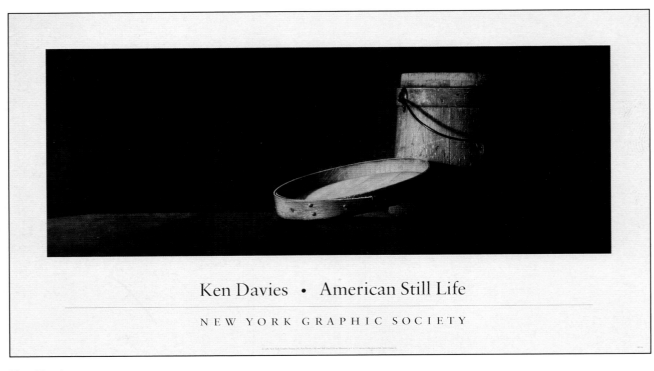

Ken Davies
OLD AND WELL USED
30159 - 20"x36" (50¾x91½ cm)

William Rice
HAWLEY'S INN
30100 - 19"x24¾" (48¼x62¾ cm)

Unknown American Artist
YOUNG BOY WITH DOG
30025 - 33"x21" (84x53½ cm)

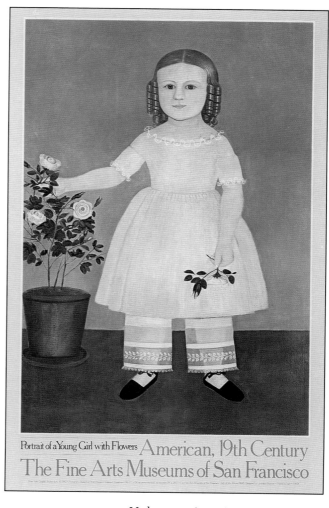

Unknown American Artist
PORTRAIT OF A YOUNG GIRL
30024 - 33"x21" (84x53½ cm)

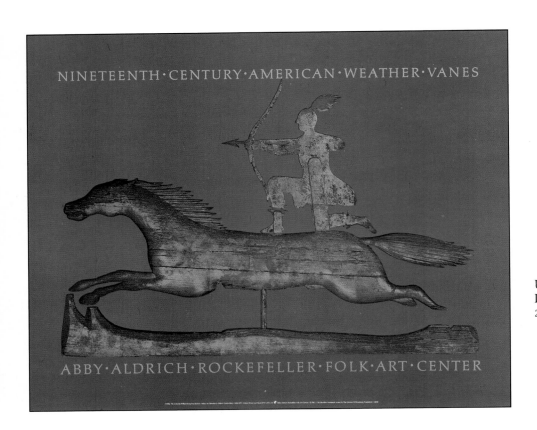

Unknown American Artist
INDIAN ON HORSEBACK WEATHERVANE
20050 - 21½"x26½" (54½x67¼ cm)

Thomas Moran
INNER GORGE OF THE GRAND CANYON
20151 - 34"x24" (86½x61 cm)

John James Audubon
GREAT BLUE HERON
20195 - 38¼″x26″ (97x66 cm)

John James Audubon
GYRFALCON
20239 - 36″x24″ (91½x61 cm)

John James Audubon
AMERICAN EGRET
20194 - 36″x24″ (91½x61 cm)

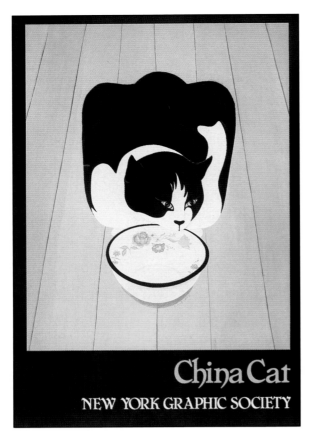

Sylvia Alberts
CHINA CAT
30126 - 30"x20" (76x50¾ cm)

Sylvia Alberts
LAKE BATHERS
30125 - 26½"x23" (67¼x58½ cm)

Robert Franke
OLD CAPE MAY
30013 - 34"x29½" (86½x75 cm)

Steven R. Miller
SAN FRANCISCO BAY WINDOWS
30103 - 25"x30" (63½x76 cm)

Eric Holch
CLIFFSIDE
30216 - 36″x24″ (91½x61 cm)

Dan Poole
RAINBOW BEACH
30014 - 36″x12″ (91½x30½ cm)

Eric Holch
FLAG DAY
30217 - 28″x32″ (71x81 cm)

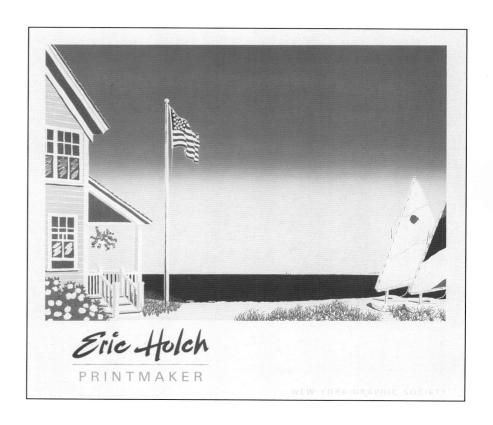

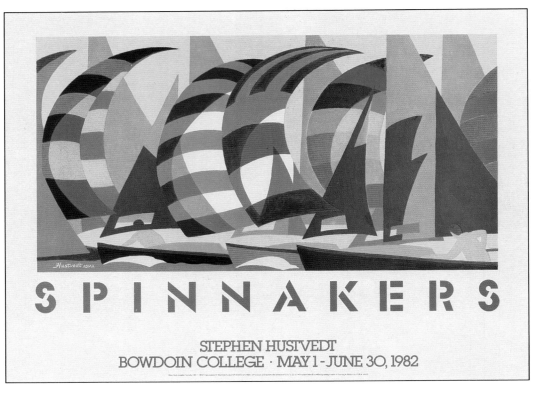

Stephen Hustvedt
SPINNAKERS
30023 - 24″x32″ (61x81 cm)

Unknown French Artist
DEAUVILLE
30019 - 38″x24″ (96½x61 cm)

Paul Nagano
AT THE CAFE
30180 - 25″x27″ (63½x68½ cm)

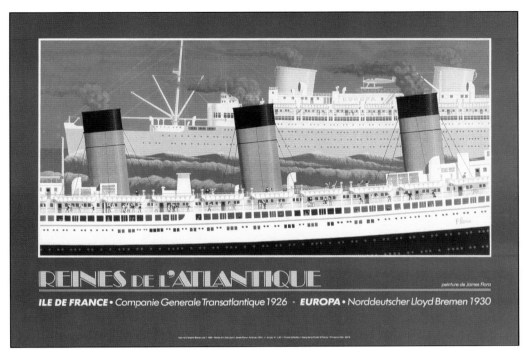

James Flora
REINES DE L'ATLANTIQUE
30018 - 22"x32" (56x81 cm)

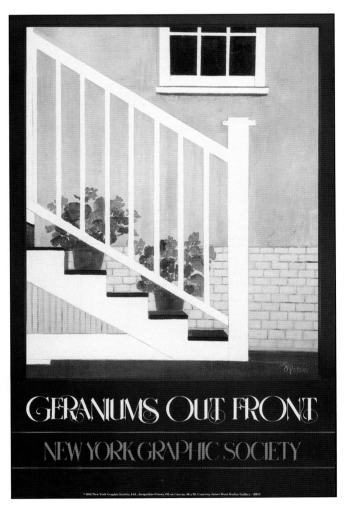

Jacqueline Peters
GERANIUMS OUT FRONT
30127 - 37"x24" (94x61 cm)

Maxfield Parrish
TWILIGHT
30007 - 33"x24" (84x61 cm)

Nan Lee
PEACEABLE KINGDOM
30010 - 28"x28" (71x71 cm)

Steven R. Miller
PENCILS WITH PATCHWORK
30049 - 36"x26" (91½x66 cm)

Herb Kornfeld
BONNIEUX
30129 - 33¼"x24" (84½x61 cm)

Victor Anonsen
TRUMPETS OF SPRING
30130 - 25"x30½" (63½x77½ cm)

Brenda Huffman
A MONUMENT TO WASHINGTON, D.C.
30041 - 35"x25" (89x63½ cm)

Brenda Huffman
A PEEK AT PALM BEACH
30042 - 35"x25" (89x63½ cm)

Brenda Huffman
ATLANTIC CITY WALTZ
30040 - 35"x25" (89x63½ cm)

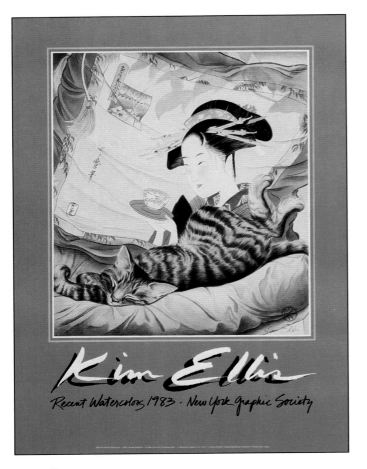

Kim Ellis
CAT NAP
30052 - 32"x24" (81x61 cm)

Joyce Sloan
GIRL TALK
30128 - 33¼"x24" (84½x61 cm)

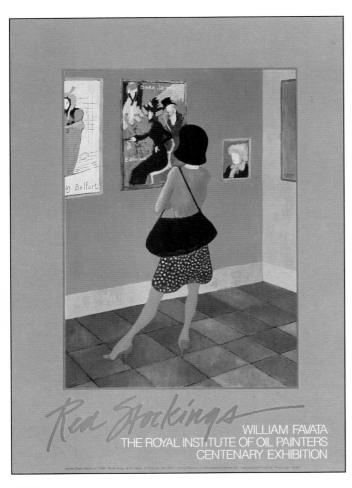

William Favata
RED STOCKINGS
30099 - 28"x20¼" (71x51½ cm)

Steinlen
DES CHATS
30104 - 28"x19½" (71x49½ cm)

Unknown French Artist
DEPOT DE CHOCOLAT
30020 - 29"x21" (73½x53½ cm)

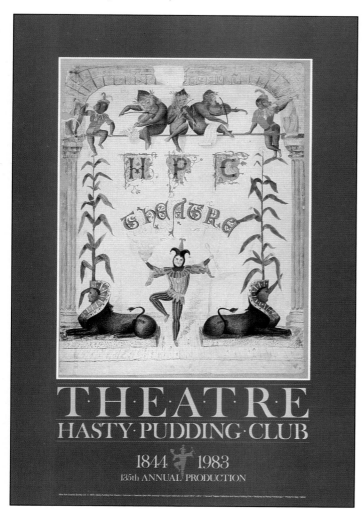

Unknown American Artist
HASTY PUDDING CLUB THEATRE
30051 - 31"x21" (78¾x53½ cm)

S.A. Weldon
THE CATNIPPERS
30053 - 32"x22" (81x56 cm)

Robert Rauschenberg
STATUE OF LIBERTY
30090 - 36"x24" (91½x61 cm)

Larry Rivers
BRONX ZOO
30094 - 24"x36" (61x91½ cm)

Red Grooms
SUBWAY RIDERS
30092 - 24"x36" (61x91½ cm)

Robert Motherwell
CULTURAL INSTITUTIONS
30093 - 36"x24" (91½x61 cm)

New York Collection

Artists Celebrate the Diversity
Most Exciting City

Alex Katz
BICYCLING IN CENTRAL PARK
30095 - 24"x36" (61x91½ cm)

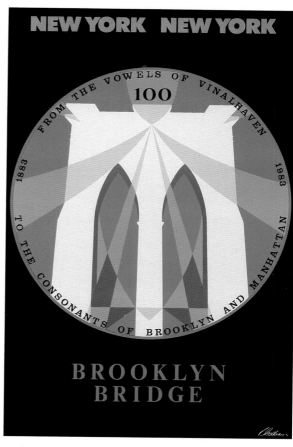

Robert Indiana
BROOKLYN BRIDGE
30091 - 36"x24" (91½x61 cm)

R.B. Kitaj
PERFORMING ARTS CENTER
30096 - 36"x24" (91½x61 cm)

James Rosenquist
COMMUNICATIONS CENTER
30097 - 24"x36" (61x91½ cm)

Barbara Newcomb
SANDY COVE, CORNWALL
30022 - 27"x30" (68½x76 cm)

Mady Daens
CARNIVAL
30021 - 37"x27" (94x68½ cm)

Wayne Thiebaud
YO-YOS
30039 - 31″x28″ (78¾x71 cm)

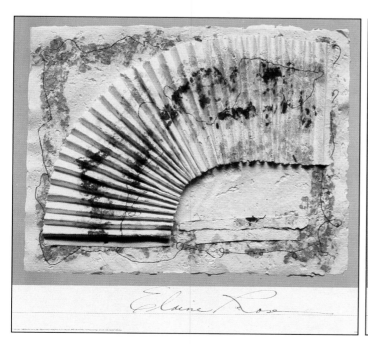
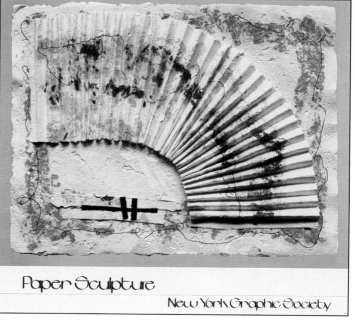

Elaine Rose
WHITE WINGS
30182 - 28″x30″ (71x76 cm)

Pierre Doutreleau
VOILES
20110 - 30"x19½" (76x49½ cm)

Pierre Doutreleau
BLUE HARBOR
20055 - 29½"x19½" (75x49½ cm)

Fanch Ledan
SAILBOATS—GOLDEN GATE BRIDGE
20102 - 30"x21½" (76x54½ cm)

Nissan Engel
LACEWORK
20149 - 35"x25¼" (89x64 cm)

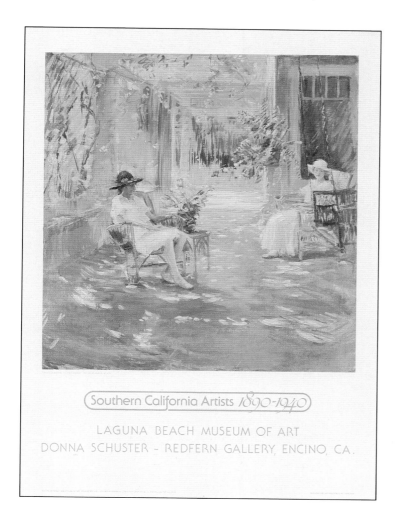

Donna A. Schuster
ON THE VERANDA
20101 - 33¼"x25" (84½x63½ cm)

Maurice Prendergast
LOW TIDE, NANTASKET
20106 - 36"x22¾" (91½x57¾ cm)

Charles Prendergast
THE RIDERS
20105 - 36"x24½" (91½x62 cm)

Joel Meyerowitz
PORCH, PROVINCETOWN
20086 - 25″x26½″ (63½x67¼ cm)

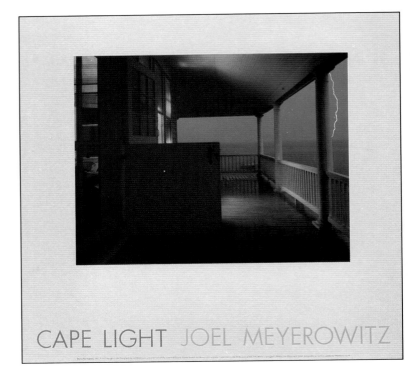

Joel Meyerowitz
COLD STORAGE BEACH, TRURO
20087 - 25″x26½″ (63½x67¼ cm)

Joel Meyerowitz
HARTWIG HOUSE
20088 - 25″x26½″ (63½x67¼ cm)

Arnold Dubnick
OAK TREE IN RAIN
30189 - 26″x24″ (66x61 cm)

Paul Caponigro
THE WISE SILENCE
30089 - 29″x27″ (73½x68½ cm)

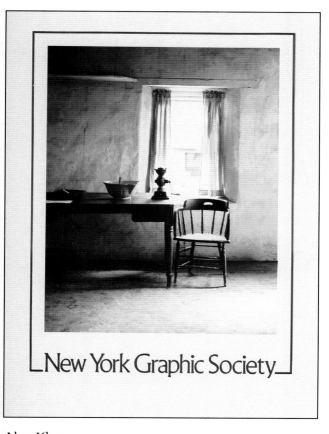

Alan Klug
MISSION HOUSE OAHU
30135 - 28½″x20¾″ (72½x52¾ cm)

Alan Klug
CALLE LE PARADISO, VENICE
30166 - 25″x30″ (63½x76 cm)

Harold Davis
WHITE WINDOW WITH FORGET-ME-NOTS
30158 - 25"x30" (63½x76 cm)

Harold Davis
OLD PLOUGH
30157 - 25"x30" (63½x76 cm)

Harold Davis
AUTUMN ISLAND
30156 - 25"x30" (63½x76 cm)

Harold Davis
CABIN BELOW, MT. RANIER, WA
30183 - 25"x30" (63½x76 cm)

Harold Davis
DANCE OF SPRING
20140 - 25"x32" (63½x81 cm)

~ The Dance of Spring is the Dance of Life ~

The Adirondacks: A Wilderness Preserved
Photographs by Harold Davis
The New-York Historical Society · March 27–June 3, 1984

Harold Davis
ADIRONDACKS
20141 - 25"x30" (63½x76 cm)

Harold Davis
DENALI—THE GREAT ONE
20142 - 25"x34½" (63½x87¾ cm)

Denali, The Great One, Alaska · Harold Davis

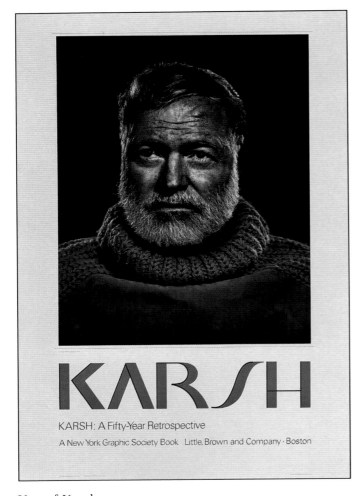

Yousef Karsh
HEMINGWAY
20122 - 34"x24" (86½x61 cm)

Edouard Boubat
PARTITION
20210 - 21¾"x20" (55¾x50¾ cm)

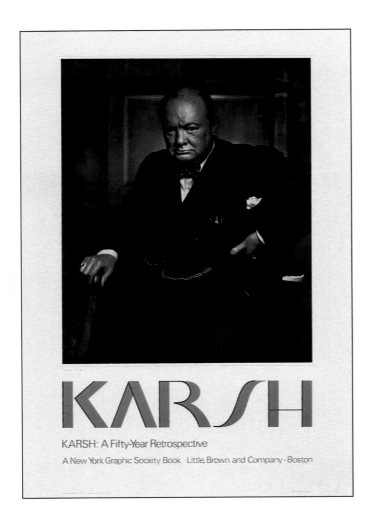

Yousef Karsh
CHURCHILL
20123 - 34"x24" (86½x61 cm)

Christo
TWO LOWER MANHATTAN WRAPPED BUILDINGS
20212 - 34½"x27" (87¾x68½ cm)

Christo
THE PONT NEUF WRAPPED
20211 - 27"x32" (68½x81 cm)

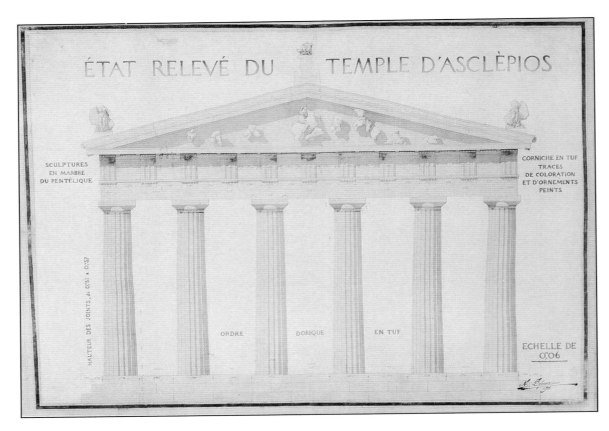

Defrasse
TEMPLE D'ASCLEPIOS
20216 - 28″x38½″ (71x97¾ cm)

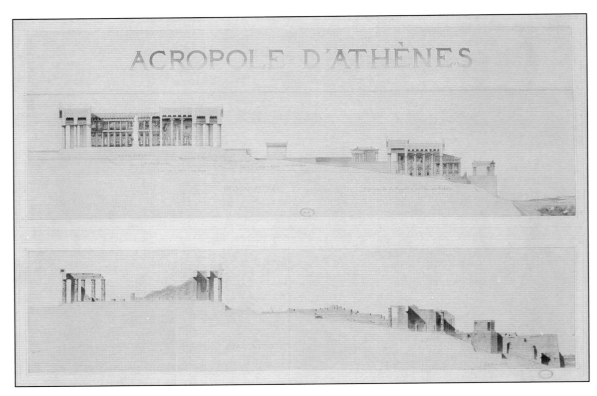

Lambert
ACROPOLE D'ATHENES
20217 - 26¾″x39″ (68x99 cm)

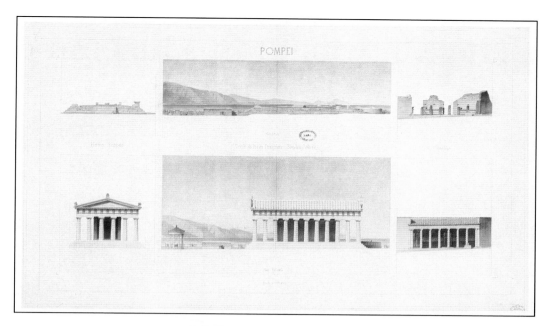

P.E. Bonnet
POMPEII ARCHITECTURE
20218 - 23¾″x39½″ (60x100¼ cm)

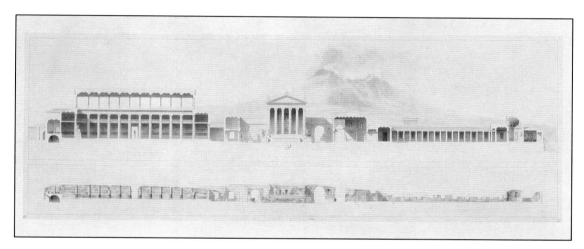

F.E. Callet
POMPEII
20154 - 19½″x47¾″ (49½x121¾ cm)

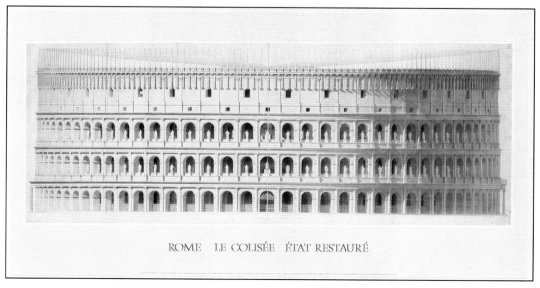

L.G. Duc
ROME LE COLISEE
20219 - 20½″x39¼″ (52x99½ cm)

From The Metropolitan Museum of Art

Chu Ling
SEATED CAT
20224 - 42"x15" (106½x38 cm)

Ch'en Shun
SUMMER GARDEN
20225 - 42"x19" (106½x48¼ cm)

Yun Shou-P'ing
LOTUS IN SUMMER EVENING
20226 - 42"x19" (106½x48¼ cm)

Unknown Chinese Artist
THREE RABBITS
20064 - 34"x23" (86½x58½ cm)

Unknown Japanese Artist
MT. FUJI IN MOONLIGHT
20223 - 31"x25" (78¾x63½ cm)

Nathaniel Currier
THE FAVORITE CAT
20043 - 39"x25" (99x63½ cm)

Vincent Van Gogh
FIRST STEPS
20237 - 30"x34" (76x86½ cm)

Vincent Van Gogh
FLOWERING GARDEN, 1888
20238 - 36"x24" (91½x61 cm)

John Gould
EMERALD HUMMINGBIRDS
20161 - 36"x20" (91½x50¾ cm)

Edouard Vuillard
GARDEN AT VAUCRESSON
20118 - 38"x24" (96½x61 cm)

John La Farge
IRISES AND WILD ROSES
20063 - 38"x24" (96½x61 cm)

Tiffany Studios
MAGNOLIAS AND IRISES
20047 - 38"x24" (96½x61 cm)

Tiffany Studios
AUTUMN LANDSCAPES
20062 - 40"x24" (101½x61 cm)

Tiffany Studios
VIEW OF OYSTER BAY
20046 - 32"x24" (81x61 cm)

William Merritt Chase
THE LAKE FOR MINIATURE SAILBOATS, CENTRAL PARK
20116 - 30″x37″ (76x94 cm)

William Merritt Chase
AT THE SEASIDE
20230 - 27″x40″ (68½x101½ cm)

Edouard Manet
A BAR AT THE FOLIES-BERGERE
20112 - 30″x34″ (76x86½ cm)

Edgar Degas
ECOLE DE DANSE
20231 - 30″x36″ (76x91½ cm)

Pierre Auguste Renoir
IN THE MEADOW
20058 - 35″x24″ (90x61 cm)

Maurice Prendergast
WOMAN PUSHING PERAMBULATOR
20232 - 42″x24″ (106½x61 cm)

Maurice Prendergast
SWINGS—REVERE BEACH
20233 - 37″x24″ (94x61 cm)

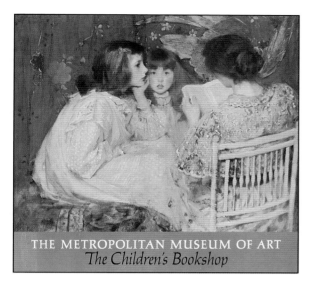

J.J. Shannon
FAIRY TALES
20060 - 30"x32" (76x81 cm)

Claude Monet
PARISIANS ENJOYING THE PARC MONCEAU
20121 - 38"x24" (96½x61 cm)

Claude Monet
TERRACE AT SAINTE-ADRESSE
20111 - 30"x33" (76x84 cm)

Claude Monet
LANDSCAPE NEAR ZAANDAM
20227 - 30"x42" (76x106½ cm)

Claude Monet
THE BEACH AT SAINTE-ADRESSE
20228 - 36"x26" (76x91½ cm)

Claude Monet
PARC MANCEAU, PARIS
20229 - 30"x37" (76x94 cm)

Edward Hopper
LIGHTHOUSE AT TWO LIGHTS
20061 - 30"x37" (76x94 cm)

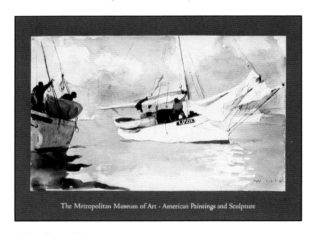

John Frederick Kensett
SUNSET, 1872
20220 - 27¾"x42" (70½x106½ cm)

Currier & Ives
THE YACHT "MOHAWK" OF NEW YORK
20221 - 28"x37" (71x94 cm)

Winslow Homer
FISHING BOAT, KEY WEST
20178 - 24"x33" (61x84 cm)

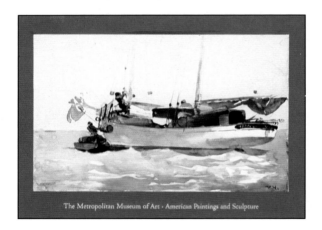

Winslow Homer
TAKING ON WET PROVISIONS, KEY WEST
20162 - 24"x33" (61x84 cm)

Winslow Homer
FLOWER GARDEN AND BUNGALOW
20222 - 24"x33" (61x84 cm)

Winslow Homer
A WALL, NASSAU
20163 - 24"x33" (61x84 cm)

Eliot Porter
TRUNKS OF MAPLE AND BIRCH WITH OAK
20036 - 34"x22" (86½x56 cm)

Eliot Porter
REDBUD TREES IN BOTTOMLAND
20037 - 34"x22" (86½x56 cm)

Eliot Porter
MIST ON THE COAST, BIG SUR
20234 - 34"x22" (86½x56 cm)

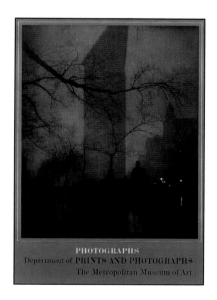

Edward J. Steichen
THE FLATIRON
20044 - 37"x25" (94x63½ cm)

Eliot Porter
WATERLILIES
20235 - 34"x22" (86½x56 cm)

Richard Estes
TELEPHONE BOOTHS
20236 - 30"x37" (76x94 cm)

ETCHINGS
and
ENGRAVINGS

An extraordinary selection of color etchings and engravings which have been published for New York Graphic Society in Europe and the United States. The images represent 17th, 18th, and 19th century master printmakers in addition to a number of well-known and talented contemporary artisans.

Each image has been printed using both original and quality re-strike plates, then individually hand-colored with meticulous attention to detail and fidelity to the original work of art.

All etchings and engravings are printed on antiqued off-white stock. Paper may differ by specific subject but care has been taken to utilize the same stock within the same image grouping. Minor differences, for which we cannot be responsible, may result due to the international nature of the program.

Dimensions provided represent the entire image to the plate mark. In all cases, these hand-colored works of art have been printed with generous borders of up to four inches to allow for elegant custom framing.

We believe this quality collection will offer numerous opportunities to serve the decorative needs of both residential and commercial areas.

English Hunting Scenes, page 573

BOTANICALS

B. Besler (1561-1628)

Plate Size: 21″x9½″
Plus Substantial Borders

IRIS LATIFOLIA
OE 5673

LILIO NARCILLUS
OE 5672

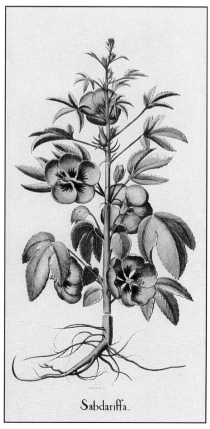

SABDARIFFA
OE 5665

LILIUM PURPUREUM
OE 5664

Available USA only

GERANIUM BATRACHIOIDES
OE 5667

MELANTHIUM HISPANICUM
OE 5666

SICILIANA
OE 5675

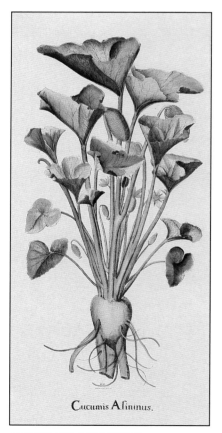

CUCUMIS AFININUS
OE 5674

Available USA only

Poma flore multiplici.

POMA FLORE
OE 5671

Aquilegia stellataflore
purpureo.

AQUILEGIA STELLATAFLORE
OE 5670

Bafilicum Indicum macu,
latum.

BAFILICUM INDICUM
OE 5668

Medium flore cœruleo.

MEDIUM FLORE COERULEO
OE 5669

BOTANICALS
B. Besler (1561-1628)

LILIUM PURPUREUM
OE 5655 - 12"x9¾"
OE 7241 - 20½"x17¾"

CORONA IMPERIALIS
OE 5654 - 12"x9¾"
OE 7229 - 20½"x17¾"

BALAUSTIA
OE 5661 - 12"x9¾"
OE 7240 - 20½"x17¾"

ALCEA SYRIACA
OE 5660 - 12"x9¾"
OE 7239 - 20½"x17¾"

Available USA only

CINERACUM FLORE
OE 5658 - 12″x9¾″
OE 7237 - 20½″x17¾″

CORONA IMPERIALIS
OE 5659 - 12″x9¾″
OE 7238 - 20½″x17¾″

TABACUM LATIFOLIUM
OE 5656 - 12″x9¾″
OE 7246 - 20½″x17¾″

CANNA INDICA RUBRA
OE 5657 - 12″x9¾″
OE 7232 - 20½″x17¾″

Available USA only

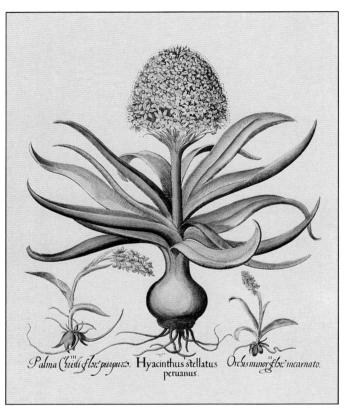

HYACINTHUS STELLATUS
OE 7231 - 20½″x17¾″

SAMBUCUS ARBORROFEA
OE 7230 - 20½″x17¾″

MELANZANA FRUCTU
OE 7235 - 20½″x17¾″

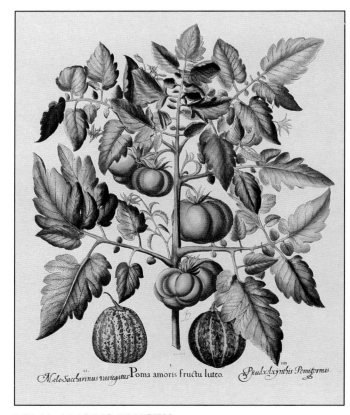

POMA AMORIS FRUCTU
OE 7236 - 20½″x17¾″

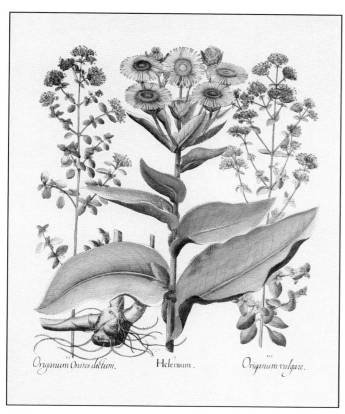

HELENIUM
OE 5653 - 12″x9¾″

POMA AURANTIA
OE 5652 - 12″x9¾″

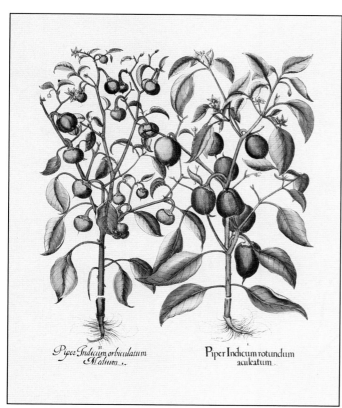

PIPER INDICUM
OE 5662 - 12″x9¾″

MELANZANA
OE 5663 - 12″x9¾″

FLORALS
G.L. Prevost (1760-1810)

OE 5542

OE 5543

OE 5541

Available USA only

Series Plate Size: 15¼″x11″
Plus Substantial Borders

OE 5415

OE 5416

OE 5417

All six images are
interchangeable and
complementary
in color

FOX HUNTING SCENES
A. Alken (1774-1850)

OE 5544   THE APPOINTMENT

OE 5545   IN FULL CRY

Available USA only

Series Plate Size: 11½″x16½″
Plus Substantial Borders

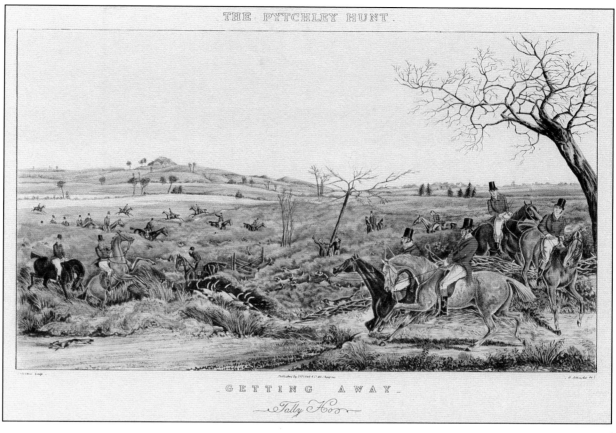

OE 5546   GETTING AWAY

OE 5547   THE DEATH

ENGLISH HUNTING SCENES
"The Right & Wrong Sort"
A. Alken (1774-1850)

Series Plate Size: 11¼″x15″
Plus Substantial Borders

OE 5625

OE 5624

OE 5623

OE 5622

OE 5620

OE 5621

Available USA only

ENGLISH HUNTING SCENES
G. Wright (1860-1942)

ON TOP OF THE MOORS
OE 5418

GAME TO THE LAST
OE 5419

8″ Diameter Circles with 2½″ Borders

THE ASHDOWNE COURSING MEETING
OE 7209

Plate Size: 15½″x35½″
Plus Substantial Border

FRENCH HORSE RACING SCENES
J. Vernet (1714-1789)

OE 7215

THE PREPARATION

OE 7216

THE DEPARTURE

Available USA only

OE 7217

THE RACE

OE 7218

AFTER THE RACE

FRENCH FOX HUNTING SCENES
G. Ripart (19th Century)

Départ pour la Chasse
(Louis XIII)

THE DEPARTURE
OE 7219

THE SPECTATORS
OE 7220

Les Honneurs

Le Rapport
(Louis XV)

THE ASSEMBLY
OE 7221

Available USA only

Series Plate Size: 10¼″x15½″
Plus Substantial Borders

THE CHASE
OE 7222

THE CALL
OE 7223

THE RETURN
OE 7224

HUNTING SCENES
G. Morland (1763-1804)

Series Plate Size: 10¼″x12¾″
Plus Substantial Borders

OE 5631   THE RABBIT HUNT

OE 5630   THE PHEASANT HUNT

OE 5633   THE PIGEON SHOOT

OE 5632   THE DUCK HUNT

SPORTING SCENES
J. Vernet (1714-1789)

Pair Plate Size: 22¼″x33½″
Plus Substantial Borders

Une Course

OE 7249   THE RACE

L'Arrivée

OE 7250   THE FINISH

ENGLISH COUNTRY SCENES

E. Douglas (19th Century)

Pair Plate Size: 30¼″x22¾″
Plus Substantial Borders

OE 7247   THE FAMILY HORSE

OE 7248   MY GUEST

Available USA only

ENGLISH COUNTRY SCENES

F.C. Turner (19th Century)

Pair Plate Size: 17¾″x20½″
Plus Substantial Borders

OE 7214   THE CLIPPER

OE 7213   THE VETERINARIAN

HUNTING DOGS
H. Alken

Series Plate Size: 12½″x10″
Plus Substantial Borders

OE 5643   COCKER SPANIEL

OE 5642   IRISH SETTER

OE 5641   ENGLISH POINTER

OE 5640   SCOTCH COLLIE

Available USA only

Pair Plate Size 7¾″x12″
Plus Substantial Borders

OE 5636   STAG HOUNDS

OE 5637   POINTERS

CARRIAGES AND COACHES
D. Diderot (1713-1784)

Series Plate Size: 9½″x11¾″
Plus Substantial Borders

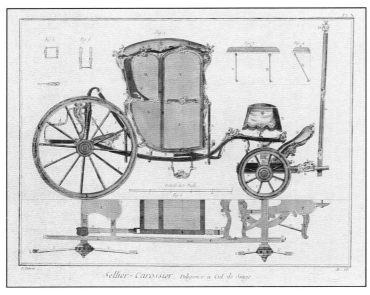

OE 5644

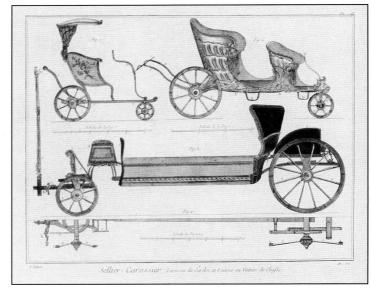

OE 5646

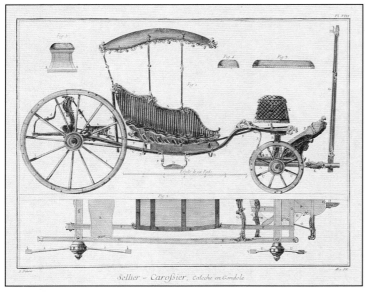

OE 5647

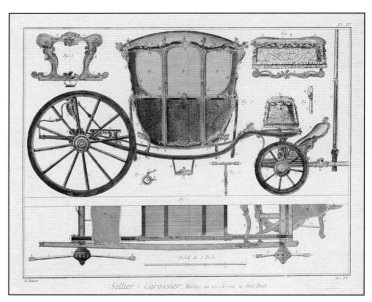

OE 5645

ENGLISH CARRIAGE SCENES

Series Plate Size: 9½"x13¾"
Plus Substantial Borders

OE 5496   TOWARDS THE HUNT

OE 5497   COMING BACK FROM HUNTING

OE 5499   DRIVING IN THE EVENING

OE 5498   DRIVING IN THE EVENING

TROTTING HORSES

The famous horse Pilot Vt while is running Record 2:19

OE 5648   PILOT

The famous horse Volunteer while is running Record 2:18¾

OE 5649   VOLUNTEER

Available USA only

The champion Electioneer in action Record 2:18

OE 5650   ELECTIONEER

The Trotting Horse Axtell interunning Record 2:19

OE 5651   AXTELL

RURAL SCENES

F. Zuccarelli (1702-1788)

Series Plate Size: 19½″x19″
Plus Substantial Borders

OE 5639   THE RURAL ITALIAN'S WEDDING

OE 5638   THE RURAL ITALIAN'S BALL

Available USA only

ENGLISH RURAL SCENES

D. Wilkie (1785-1841)

Pair Plate Size: 19¾"x24¾"
Plus Substantial Borders

OE 7251   BLIND MAN'S BLUFF

OE 7252   THE BLIND FIDDLER

ENGLISH COUNTRY HOMES

W. Angus (1752-1821)

HARE HALL
OE 5610

BROOME HALL
OE 5613

MILTON MANOR
OE 5615

Series Plate Size: 8¾″x12″
Plus Substantial Borders

MOCCAS COURT
OE 5611

LARTINGTON HALL
OE 5614

HOLLAND HOUSE
OE 5612

FRENCH CHATEAUX
18th Century

Series Plate Size: 7½″x10½″
Plus Substantial Borders

OE 5607   CARROUGES

OE 5608   LION SUR-MER

OE 5606   GRATOT

OE 5609   BOISSEY LE CHATEL

Available USA only

ENGLISH COUNTRY LANDSCAPES
B.W. Leader (19th Century)

THE GLEAM BEFORE THE STORM
OE 7245
Plate Size: 18¼"x27½"
Plus Substantial Border

BY MEAD AND STREAM
OE 7244
Plate Size: 17"x28½"
Plus Substantial Border

THE WAY TO THE VILLAGE CHURCH
OE 7243
Plate Size: 17¾"x27"
Plus Substantial Border

Available USA only

VENETIAN SCENES

A. Zuccagni-Orlandini (1784-1872)

Series Plate Size: 9"x12¼"
Plus Substantial Borders

OE 5617   DUCAL PALACE

OE 5616   RIALTO BRIDGE

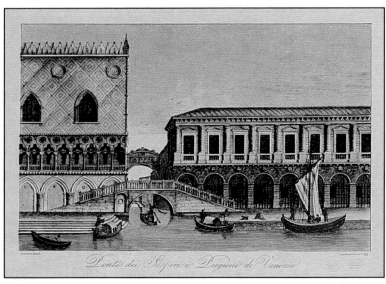

OE 5618   BRIDGE OF SIGHS

OE 5619   CHURCH OF SANTA MARIA

Available USA only

GREAT SAILING SHIPS

P.C. Canot (Dutch, 1710-1777)

Series Plate Size: 15½"x19½"
Plus Substantial Borders

OE 7234   A BRISK GALE

OE 7233   GALLEONS AT ANCHOR

ANCIENT SAILING VESSELS
C. Randon (1674-1704)

OE 7227   LA VOITTE

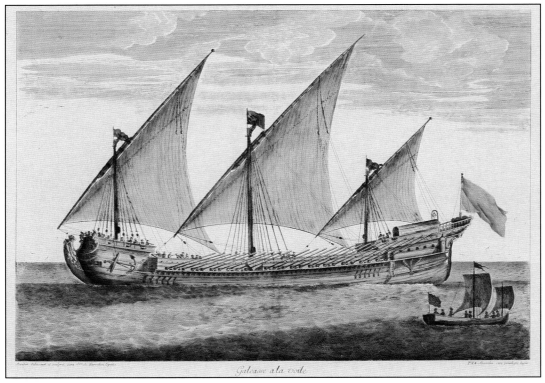

OE 7226   LA VOILE

OE 7228   LA FONDE

OE 7225   LA RAME

19th CENTURY CLIPPER SHIPS
N. Diana (19th Century)

OE 5501   GREAT BRITAIN

OE 5503   NORMANDIE

Available USA only

Series Plate Size: 10″x15″
Plus Substantial Borders

OE 5500

TORRENS

OE 5502

ARGO

17th CENTURY ASTRONOMICAL MAPS
K. Cellario (1638-1707)

OE 7210   GRAPHIA MATIS

OE 7208   PLANISPHAERIUM

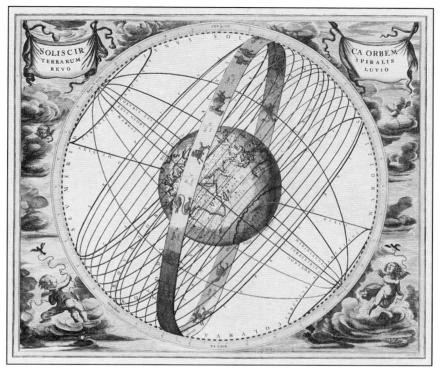

OE 7211   ORBEM SPIRALIS

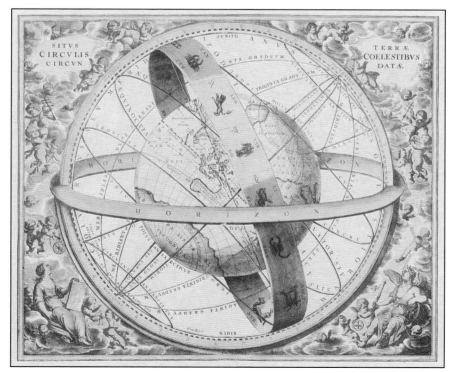

OE 7207   SITUS CIRCULIS

ANTIQUE AMERICAN MAPS

J. Blaeu (1556-1673)

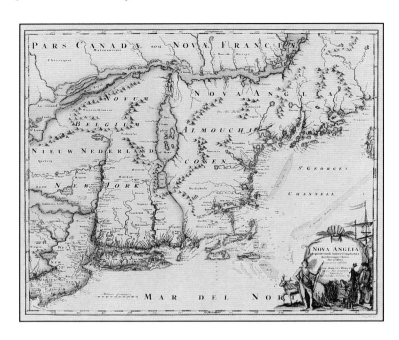

NOVA ANGLIA
OE 7253
Plate Size: 17"x20¼"
Plus Substantial Border

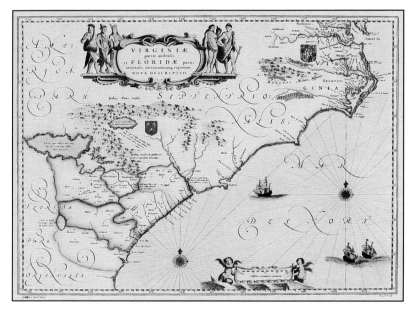

VIRGINIAE ET FLORIDAE
OE 7254
Plate Size: 17"x21½"
Plus Substantial Border

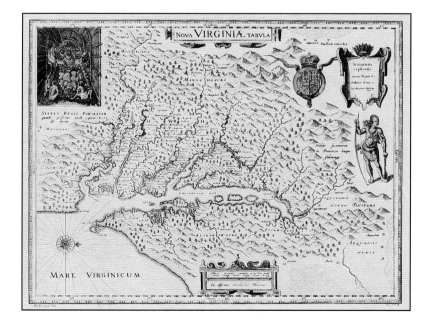

MARE VIRGINICUM
OE 7255
Plate Size: 17"x21½"
Plus Substantial Border

ENGLISH MILITARY COSTUMES

J. Rowlandson (1756-1827)

Series Plate Size: 9¾″x6½″
Plus Substantial Borders

OE 5603   DEPTFORD

OE 5604   VINTRY WARD

OE 5601   COLEMAN STREET

OE 5600   EAST INDIA

OE 5605   HIGHLANDER

OE 5602   LAMBETH

OE 5504   PARIS, JUSTICE PALACE

THE
Franz X. Wolf
COLLECTION

Austrian (1896-)

A selection of original color etchings pencil-signed by the artist from plates completed between the years 1926 and 1946. Each impression is an original work of art produced from individual color plates. The images have been created by the artist using only traditional hand-pulled etching techniques.

The recipient of many awards during the course of his long career, Franz Wolf is one of the very few artists listed in all major fine etching reference works during his lifetime.

OE 5505   PARIS, GREENGROCER

Pair Plate Size: 12¼″x9½″
Plus Substantial Borders

Available USA only

Franz X. Wolf

OE 5551 - 11½″x14¼″   PARIS, BIRD MARKET

OE 5634 - 14¼″x12″ PARIS, NOTRE DAME AND BOOKSTALLS

Plus Substantial Borders

OE 5629 - 10¾″x12¾″ PARIS, BOOKSTALLS WITH TERRIER

Franz X. Wolf

OE 5412 - 12½″×14¼″   VENICE, MARIA DELLA SALUTE

Plus Substantial Borders

OE 5411 - 12½″×16″   VENICE, CA D'ORO

Available USA only

Franz X. Wolf

OE 5626 - 13⅛″x16½″   VENICE SAILBOATS

Plus Substantial Borders

OE 5627 - 16¾″x13″   ST. WOLFGANG   OE 5628 - 16¾″x13″   HALLSTATT

ORIGINAL HAND-COLORED
WILDLIFE ETCHINGS
by Dan Mitra

Each Image Pencil-Signed by the Artist

OE 7140   MALLARD DUCKS

Duck Image Plate Size 25″x31″ Plus Substantial Borders

OE 7141   WOOD DUCKS

Available USA only

European-born artist Dan Mitra has created these true-to-life wildlife prints with extraordinary attention to anatomical detail and natural colors. Each is an original hand-pulled etching which has been individually hand-colored and pencil-signed by the artist.

These attractively priced etchings will add an expensive decorator look to both residential and commercial interiors.

OE 7136   PINTAIL

OE 7137   MALLARD

Duck Image Plate Size 16″x21″
Fish and Lure Image Plate Size 14″x20″

Plus Substantial Borders

OE 7139   WHITE BASS

OE 7138   LARGE MOUTH BASS

Available USA only

SEA SHELLS
by Dan Mitra

**Each Panel 32″x8″ Vertical, Plus Substantial Borders
Shells may be Separated and Framed Individually**

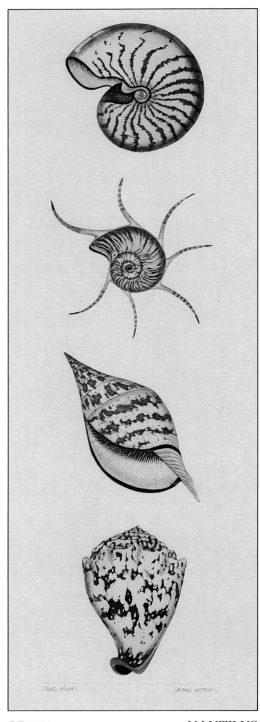

OE 7260   NAUTILUS

OE 7261   SCALLOP

Available USA only

INDEX

NUMERICAL INDEX   617

618   NUMERICAL INDEX

POSTERS

ETCHINGS and ENGRAVINGS

Editor-in-Chief: Lawrence Tolchin
Art Director & Production Manager: Caron Caswell
Cover Design: David Cundy Inc.
New Photography: Gamma One Conversions
Typography & Printing: Eastern Press, Inc.
Binding: Tappley-Rutter Company, Inc.
Composition in Melior and Melior Bold
Text: Printed on 65# Warrenflo